D1405093

ABOUT THIS SERIES

The ultimate responsibility for determining the fate of this nation rests with its citizens. Given that responsibility, they must inform themselves so they can make wise decisions. For U.S. citizens to do this, however, requires that they have access to facts and knowledge essential to the decision-making process. We must share in the responsibility by making information readily accessible to the public.

Because of the complexity and seriousness of the problems facing our nation today, special public communications efforts are needed more than before. This series represents one such effort by a basic industry, the nation's electric utility companies, through Edison Electric Institute.

Decisionmakers Bookshelf seeks to provide to the public important discussions and reasoned viewpoints on national policy problems related to energy.

ABOUT EEI

Edison Electric Institute is the association of America's investor-owned electric utility companies. Organized in 1933 and incorporated in 1970, EEI provides a principal forum where electric utility people exchange information on developments in their business, and maintain liaison between the industry and the federal government. Its officers act as spokesmen for investor-owned electric utility companies on subjects of national interest.

Since 1933, EEI has been a strong, continuous stimulant to the art of making electricity. A basic objective is the "advancement in the public service of the art of producing, transmitting, and distributing electricity and the promotion of scientific research in such field." EEI ascertains factual information, data, and statistics relating to the electric industry, and makes them available to member companies, the public, and government representatives.

ELECTRICITY:
SOURCES AND
TECHNOLOGIES

CONTENTS

NUCLEAR POWER—ANSWERS TO YOUR QUESTIONS

CONTENTS

CONTENTS

CONTENTS

CONTENTS

CONTENTS

NUCLEAR POWER

ANSWERS TO YOUR QUESTIONS

THE NEED FOR NUCLEAR POWER

Our nation relies on electricity to meet a wide variety of its energy needs, from heating homes in the winter and cooling them in the summer to running factories. Nuclear power plays an important role in insuring that the nation can depend on an adequate, reliable electricity supply. In the future, the United States will need to rely even more heavily on nuclear power to meet increased electricity demand.

How much electricity do we use?

To light our homes and streets, to power our factories and farms, to operate our hospitals and schools and to make possible all the uses of electricity our society demands required 2,286,439,000,000 kilowatt-hours (kwh) in 1980.

In 1981, total generation of electricity is expected to be 1.5 to 2.5 percent greater, a growth rate considerably below the 7 percent annual rate that prevailed until the mid-1970s. This figure reflects slow economic conditions and the American people's efforts to conserve and make wise use of all forms of energy. Still, there has been and will be continued growth in electricity consumption, and the 1980 census showed there are now more people—226 million at that count—who depend upon an adequate supply of electricity to support their jobs and living standards and to make possible many of their goals in life.

There are reasons other than population growth for the continued increase in electricity consumption. Most people want the health, labor-saving benefits and enjoyment of electrically powered devices, from washing machines to air conditioning to TV and laser beam surgery, resulting in increased demand. Electricity is vital to cleaning up the environment, too: for example, it pumps water in sewage treatment plants, destroys bacteria, and operates equipment that removes pollutants from industrial emissions. Even the simple "energy self-sufficient" life requires great amounts of central station electricity. For example, solar energy collectors being researched and tested by many—electric companies included—are made mostly of aluminum and glass—both highly energy-intensive materials.

Electricity consumption continues to increase despite considerable efforts to conserve, and recovery of the U.S. economy would mean additional power demands well above present levels. The most authoritative projections of the future use of electricity (see *Choice over Chance*, available in most public libraries or by writing EEI) estimate an annual growth in electricity generation between 2.0 percent and 4.3 percent, to a total of 5.5 trillion kilowatt-hours in 2000, double the amount used today. New technologies such as electric cars or widespread use of home computers would be in addition to this projected growth.

Producing the power Americans need, reliably delivered at reasonable cost, will require electric companies to make use of all feasible electric generating technologies, all their ingenuity, capital, knowledge, and other resources.

Can electricity replace oil?

One factor that has driven everyone's energy bills up is the high cost of oil. Dependence on imported oil threatens national security, too. Electricity generated economically by domestic coal, nuclear, water, and other energy sources can be substituted for many purposes for which we now use oil. But economic and political factors affect the extent to which substitution can be made.

The displacement of oil by other energy sources can be obvious or hidden. An oil-fired electric generating station might be replaced by a nuclear or coal-fired unit, thus obviously displacing oil. Many times the displacement is more subtle. For example, a new glass or metal-making company, depending on cost factors, might decide to use electric instead of oil furnaces. Such a decision would not show on any records as a substitution of electricity generated by nuclear or coal for oil. Nor would a homebuilder's choice of an electric heat pump instead of an oil burner.

A recent article addressing Europe's staggering dependence on imported oil (90 percent is imported) pointed out, "the principal reason for the growth (in Western Europe's electrical energy capacity) is that electricity is supplanting direct oil burning in many end uses, and thus is reducing—albeit slowly—Europe's dependence on petroleum imports."

In Canada, the practical ability of electricity to replace imported oil was examined in a study, "Electricity/Oil Substitution," published in late 1980. It concludes that Canada, with about one-third of U.S. import dependence, could totally eliminate oil imports in 15 years by substituting electricity for oil.

The ability of electricity, which can be produced from numerous sources, to replace oil directly and indirectly is the primary driving force behind the aggressive nuclear-electric programs of France, Japan, Korea, Spain, Belgium, Sweden, Switzerland, Finland, Bulgaria, and Czechoslovakia.

There are four principal areas in which other sources of energy can replace oil: generation of electricity, residential heating, industrial heating, and transportation.

Generation of Electricity: The United States consumed about 1.2 million barrels of oil a day in 1980 to generate electricity. The majority of this oil was imported. With 92 percent of this oil used for baseload generation, it is technically feasible to substitute the far less expensive and more readily available alternatives of coal and nuclear energy.

Residential Heating: The United States consumes about 1.4 million barrels of oil a day to provide heat in residences. Technically, all of this could be replaced with electricity, natural gas, and solar power. As far as electricity is concerned, exhaustive studies at the Argonne National Laboratories have shown electric heat pumps (which are solar devices that make use of the sun's heat trapped in the air and ground) are one of the most economic means of home heating.

Industrial Heating: A preliminary study published in 1979 by the Oak Ridge National Laboratory found that "existing technology will permit substitution of electricity for approximately 75 percent of the natural gas and petroleum now being consumed by industrial processors." There would clearly be economic, legislative, and practical limitations to achieving this potential, but it is nonetheless impressive, amounting to savings of almost 3 million barrels of oil a day.

Electricity can economically substitute for the use of fossil fuels in a long list of industrial processes. Interestingly, for example, recent testimony presented to the U.S. Senate described a process for melting glass that uses electrical energy three times more efficiently than the energy from natural gas.

Transportation: The dream of an electric car is appealing to many, but is unlikely to require new electric generating plants, at least in the short term. The major breakthrough needed in developing such a car is a battery that is inexpensive, light-weight and capable of storing larger amounts of energy than today's batteries. Since the batteries would be recharged at night, when there is little demand on existing plants, customers would benefit, as would electric companies, by using idle electric capacity already installed.

There are already applications where electric vehicles make sense and save oil. The United States Postal Service electric trucks, by the Post Office's own figures, cost 39 percent less to operate and use 20 percent less energy than is required for gasoline-powered trucks.

The Department of Energy goal to have 10 percent of all cars, vans and trucks electric-powered by the year 2000 would save about 500,000 barrels of precious oil a day.

How does nuclear power aid in meeting our needs for electricity?

Nuclear production of electricity is significant right now and has the potential of becoming more significant in the future.

Eleven percent of electric generation was provided by nuclear units in commercial operation by the end of 1980. Coal provided the most, about 50.8 percent; oil, 10.8 percent; natural gas, 15.1 percent; and water power, 12.1 percent. It is expected that nuclear again will surpass oil as a source of electricity in 1981.

The nuclear percentage will increase substantially because over 50 percent of the new electric generating units now scheduled for future operation are nuclear. Almost all the rest of the new plants are coal-fired. Together, coal and nuclear power are viewed as the nation's best hope for drastically cutting oil consumption, freeing supplies of that increasingly expensive resource for its many other uses.

By 1990, 77 additional nuclear units totaling 88,000 megawatts (mw) of

3

capacity are expected to bring the nuclear total to about 25 percent of all electric energy required in the United States.

Looking at the total contribution of nuclear power as a national average, however, obscures the fact that many areas are vitally dependent on this energy source. For example, one-third of the electricity generated in New England in 1980 came from nuclear power, with the percentage as high as 78 percent in Vermont.

Nuclear energy has been widely adopted for electricity production in some states, because they are located in regions that historically have depended on imported oil and have few significant indigenous energy alternatives, such as coal. There are many other reasons, of course, including the need to have balanced sources of fuel to assure system reliability in case one source is interrupted, the need to meet clean air regulations and the need to adjust for changes in the cost and availability of fuel transportation.

The National Electric Reliability Council (NERC) states that during 1980–89, the nuclear share of electricity will increase from the present 22 percent to 41 percent in the Mid-Atlantic region, from 22 percent to 40 percent in Mid-America, from 25 percent to 36 percent in the Northeast and from 22 percent to 40 percent in the Southeast.

The United States is not alone in expanding use of commercial nuclear energy. Many foreign countries are looking increasingly to nuclear power to lessen the vulnerability of dependence on imported oil. The executive director of the International Energy Agency has called for significant nuclear expansion, because 30 percent of all electricity produced in Western nations is oil-fired. He has said the International Energy Agency believes nuclear can increase from "today's 100,000 mw (in the 18 participating nations) to 485,000 mw in 2000, at which time it would comprise 15 percent of total energy requirements as against 4 percent today."

Currently, nuclear energy supplies 23 percent of the electricity in Belgium, 22 percent in Sweden, 20 percent in France, 13 percent in the United Kingdom, 12 percent in West Germany, 14 percent in Japan, 9 percent in Canada, and 3 percent in the Soviet Union. France and the Soviet Union have the largest commitments for increases in nuclear capacity by 2000.

Why do we need more nuclear power?

Virtually all major energy studies, including those by the authoritative National Academy of Sciences, Resources for the Future, and the Ford Foundation, agree that even with serious and successful conservation, energy demand will grow at least 30 percent by 2000 if economic growth is maintained at the average rate achieved since the Arab oil embargo of 1973–74. New energy supplies will be essential on a larger scale to fuel an economy that must expand to accommodate people entering the job market and requiring goods and services over the next 20 years. For every three workers today, there will be four in 2000. It is estimated that we will use as much energy over the next 20 years as we have since the American Revolution.

Where will the additional energy come from? Clearly, national interest dictates that the United States reduce, not increase, its reliance on foreign oil. Domestic oil is limited. Studies that have examined in detail all aspects of the United States' energy future conclude almost without exception that alternative energy sources such as solar, wind, and geothermal can contribute no more than 5 percent of our total energy needs through the end of this century. Nonetheless, this would be an impressive increase, hundreds of times greater than the 1980 contribution from these sources.

Clearly then, significant "new" sources of energy must be found. The most certain are electricity generated by hydropower, coal, and nuclear energy. The upper limits for hydro's contribution in this country have been reached, and the well-publicized rebuilding of old, small hydro plants can contribute only a small fraction of future needs. Coal, on the other hand, offers enormous potential, although it is questionable whether it can be mined and transported in sufficient quantity to meet all the demands placed on it by a growing synthetic fuels industry, an expanding export market and the utility industry. Environmental concerns impose additional constraints on rapid coal expansion, emphasizing the need for the United States to have a diverse energy mix rather than dependency on any single source.

Nuclear energy is an ideal component of our energy supply in the face of these realities. It offers significant advantages:

- It is a proven, "homegrown" technology with a record of safety excellence dating back to 1957, when the first commercial nuclear station went into service.
- It uses uranium, an indigenous and relatively inexpensive fuel that has essentially only one commercial use: the production of electricity.
- It is the cleanest source of energy for steam electric plants, emitting neither smoke, soot, nor fumes.
- Ultimately, it offers the prospect of a virtually unlimited energy supply by means of breeder reactors, which create more fuel than they consume.

But isn't there an excess of electrical capacity?

The national average reserve margin today is about 32 percent but varies widely across the nation. Some regions are close to being below the minimum recommended for reliable service—typically 20 percent. Furthermore, this single statistic can be misleading if viewed in isolation from the total environment and responsibilities facing electricity suppliers.

The seemingly ample reserves could be quite illusory. Much of this generating capacity is oil-fired, so to hold down customers' bills the companies use those plants as little as possible. NERC estimates that less than 19 percent of the nation's total electric capacity (as contrasted to reserve) will be oil-fired in 1989 as compared with 27 percent in 1979. This reduction, however, will be possible only if presently planned coal and nuclear stations are completed on time—otherwise, the United States could use *more* oil for electricity generation in 1990.

Other factors that will erode present reserve margins:

—Conservation and wise use have slowed the growth rate, but more electricity is being used each year.

—Many companies, principally because of low earnings, lack the financial ability to build new plants to replace old generating units as they wear out.

—Economic recovery or prolonged hot or cold weather could cause huge increases in electricity use.

—The length of time it takes to build a new nuclear (up to 14 years) or coal plant (up to 12 years) could see the existing reserve used up before new plants are available.

Today's reserve margin arose, despite many cancellations and postponements, from the installation of generating equipment ordered as much as 10 years ago, combined with the lower than expected growth in consumption since 1974. Although this resulted in more reserve capacity than the optimum, when inflation is taken into consideration, these earlier-ordered plants today are real bargains.

Electric utilities attempt to maintain adequate reserve margins, too, because they participate in power-sharing agreements with neighboring utilities, primarily on a regional basis. Such arrangements cover virtually the entire continental United States.

The purpose of these regional compacts is to maximize the available power from operating plants, using the lowest-cost or "baseload" generation first—usually coal, nuclear, or hydro—and turning to the more expensive oil-fired or "peaking stations" only at times of peak demand.

This way, customers' bills are minimized to the benefit of all and chances of costly and potentially dangerous disruptions in service are reduced. If a member suffers equipment failure, overload, fuel supply problems, drought, or other extreme weather conditions, it can call on the power pool for needed electricity. In fact, without the reserve margins available in the southwestern United States to power air conditioners during the record heat wave of 1980, the heat-related death toll could have been much higher.

Why do utilities support nuclear power development?

Utilities are required by law to supply electricity to all at the lowest reasonable cost on a reliable and dependable basis. Utilities do this in several ways: by burning coal, oil, or natural gas; utilizing nuclear energy; or constructing dams for the development of hydro-electric power.

Which of these energy sources is used in what proportion is dictated by the resources available to the utility and numerous other practical considerations. For instance, utilities in the Northeast developed water power very early in their histories because it was easily available to them. When practically all the economic dam sites were fully developed, and need for power kept growing, they turned to coal. Then, when air pollution regulations and transportation difficulties turned against more use of coal, they turned to oil. Then, the cost and supply problems of oil gave the economic advantage to nuclear energy. Another utility in a different region might have made the choice to construct coal-fired plants all along.

The fact is that utilities must base business decisions on economics, not on personal preferences or partisanship, and they do so under restrictions imposed by regulatory commissions. In some cases, a decision based on the facts favors nuclear; in others, coal or some other source.

Why not look to alternative sources, such as solar energy?

Utilities have not ruled out the potential that alternative sources of energy, such as the sun, may have to offer with time and technical innovation. In fact, through the Electric Power Research Institute (EPRI) and in cooperation with various government research programs, most utilities are contributing to the necessary research that must precede the introduction of alternative systems. When alternative sources prove economically feasible and practical, they will be included in a utility's generating mix or be attractive to individuals. In fact, in limited areas of the West where there is geothermal energy, utilities already are using this power source and developing others.

The electric power industry has an awesome responsibility: to supply the increasing amounts of electricity needed to provide an expanding population with jobs, services, food, housing, material goods, and health. It is not a business in which desperate gambles can be taken.

Moreover, even major breakthroughs in emerging technologies take time to develop, manufacture and build. To protect consumers, a new system also would have to meet cost and reliability factors. The energy needs cited in earlier paragraphs would occur long before any new technology could mature, and those who must make decisions now for the future have concluded that the two major available economic sources which must be developed are coal and nuclear power.

Do Americans support nuclear power?

Poll after poll of national opinion has shown a majority of the American public supports nuclear energy. Even six months after the accident at Three Mile Island, a poll by Louis Harris and Associates found Americans would support building more nuclear plants by 52 to 37 percent. Over the past few years, repeated surveys consistently reveal that some two-thirds of the public opposes closing nuclear stations. A late 1980 survey by pollster Pat Caddell showed that 81 percent agreed the Three Mile Island accident was an isolated incident that did not reflect a basic structural problem with nuclear power. Fifty-four percent felt plant safety had improved as a result of the accident.

Surveys conducted by qualified, independent research organizations such as Louis Harris, Roper Reports, the Department of Energy, Cambridge Reports, and others over the past decade indicate continuing support for nuclear. Regions where operating nuclear plants are located tend to show strong voter support for these facilities.

How do nuclear power plants hold down electric costs?

In 1980, Edison Electric Institute estimated the costs of producing electricity were 2.25 cents for a kwh generated from nuclear, 2.4 cents for a kwh from coal, and 6 cents for a kwh from oil.

The construction costs of a nuclear plant are higher than those of a coal-fired station, although the array of pollution-control equipment now required on coal plants is pushing those costs up, too. A large electric generating station, whether coal or nuclear, costs $1 to $1.5 billion. These costs represent an investment of $3,500 to $5,000 for each person served, but a station will provide electricity for 30 or more years.

Nuclear power inherently offers prodigious savings in fuel costs. The costs of coal, oil, and gas have risen tremendously because of supply limitations, the difficulty of getting them out of the ground and the cost of transportation. Some utilities, for example, have found the cost of fuel has more than doubled in two years. With oil-fired stations, over 70 percent of the cost of producing electricity is related to fuel expenses alone. With coal, over 50 percent of the cost of the electricity production is fuel-related. However, nuclear fuel accounts for less than 25 percent of the total electricity production cost. For this reason, nuclear power is *partially* insulated from future cost inflation and *somewhat* insulated from whatever difficulties might arise in mining or transportation.

The cost of nuclear fuel is relatively low for two reasons. First, instead of a steady stream of fuel deliveries (2 million tons or 20,000 railcars of coal, or 10 million barrels of oil a year for comparable fossil plants), nuclear fuel is delivered to a plant site once each year or two. Second, uranium is a compact source of vast amounts of energy: a single pound of reactor uranium fuel produces as much electricity as about 90,000 pounds of coal.

The key point is that the price of oil has soared from a little under $5 a barrel in 1973 to well over $20 a barrel in 1980, according to the Department of Energy, and this has made oil-fired electricity highly expensive.

Therefore, when fuel costs are considered, many utilities that have coal, oil, gas, and nuclear stations available try to run the nuclear and coal units as much as possible to achieve cost savings to their customers. The other units are run only on an as-needed basis. Oil plants, for which fuel is expensive, and some pumped-storage hydro stations are used ideally for "peaking power." That is, they are operated when electric demand is unusually high; for example, on the hottest days of summer or coldest days of winter, when customer use exceeds the supply put out by nuclear, coal, or other "baseload" plants.

It is unlikely that any energy costs will decrease in the future. For a variety of reasons, but especially because of inflation, all energy is likely to cost more. However, the nuclear component of a balanced system will help minimize those increases. As expensive as electricity seems today, its average increase in cost to consumers is less than the general increase in the cost of living—127 points above 1967 versus 147 points for the Cost of Living Index.

NUCLEAR POWER PRODUCTION

To understand the basics of nuclear power production, it is necessary to explain the characteristics of atoms. An atom is made up of a nucleus containing positively charged protons and uncharged neutrons, orbited by negatively charged electrons, much as planets revolve around the sun. Normally, as with the poles of a magnet, protons being of a like charge, repel each other. However, in the nucleus, a special "glue," called the "binding force," holds protons and neutrons together. The strength of this binding force varies from atom to atom. If this force is weak enough, it can be overcome, and then the nucleus (therefore, the atom) can be split.

There are many types of uranium atoms or isotopes, all virtually identical chemically, but each with a subtle difference; each has a slightly different number of neutral particles (neutrons). In nature, uranium consists of several isotopes with slightly differing atomic weights, but principally of uranium-238 (99.3 percent) and uranium-235 (0.7 percent). The isotope numbers refer to the total number of particles in the nucleus. The uranium-235 nucleus is quite unstable, with a weaker binding force, and can be split or "fissioned" by hitting it with a neutron. The uranium-238 nucleus has a stronger binding force, making it much more difficult to fission, and is thus often called "non-fissionable."

When hit by a neutron, the uranium-235 nucleus fissions—splits into two or more new elements. This process releases heat, radiation, and two or three more neutrons. Under controlled conditions, these other neutrons can strike other uranium-235 atoms and cause them to split, releasing more neutrons, splitting more atoms, and so on. Thereby, continuous fissioning can take place—a chain reaction. In nuclear power reactors, the heat that accompanies this process is then used to produce high- temperature steam, which is used to generate electricity.

Nuclear fission does, in fact, occur spontaneously in nature, but those natural occurrences cannot sustain themselves because the freed neutrons are absorbed by non-fissionable atoms or just quickly decay. A nuclear reactor, by contrast, minimizes this loss of neutrons and can achieve continuous fissioning (a chain reaction) by using fuel that is free of impurities that might absorb the vital neutrons; by increasing the concentration of the rarer fissionable uranium-235 atoms (concentrations of 2 to 3 percent are typical in United States reactors); and by slowing neutrons down by providing a "moderator." In United States commercial reactors, the primary cooling water in the reactor also serves as the moderator.

Fissioning one uranium atom releases 50 million times more energy than the combustion of a single carbon atom common to all fossil fuels (coal, oil, or natural gas). Since there are trillions upon trillions of atoms in a single, tiny reactor fuel pellet, the number of fissions achieved and the energy released are impressive. Three small fuel pellets, each about the size of the end of a little finger, can provide enough electricity for a family of four for a year. Equivalent electrical energy would require 3.5 tons of coal or 12 barrels of oil.

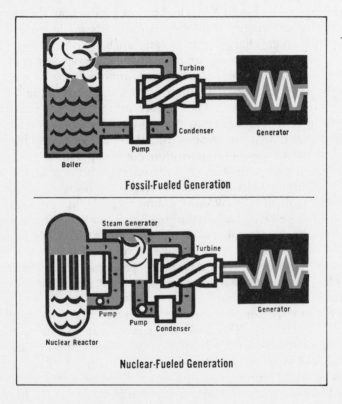

Fossil-Fueled Generation

Nuclear-Fueled Generation

How does a reactor work?

In a hydro-electric plant, the weight of falling water is used to turn a turbine generator to produce electricity. In a fossil-fuel power plant, coal, oil, or gas burned in a furnace provides heat to change water to high-temperature steam. This intensely hot (about 1050°F) "energy filled" steam drives the blades of a turbine which spins a generator, producing electricity. In a nuclear power plant, the furnace is replaced by a reactor containing a core of nuclear fuel, primarily uranium. Heat is produced in the reactor by splitting uranium atoms and used to make the steam.

10

There are four essential parts of a commercial reactor:

(1) The core contains the fissionable nuclear fuel assemblies. Each assembly consists of a number of metal tubes in which are tiny cylindrical ceramic pellets containing uranium. The assemblies are held in carefully designed geometric arrays by grid plates. A typical reactor fuel core is a cylindrical shape of about 12 feet in diameter and 12 feet high.

(2) The control system serves to regulate the rate of fission and, thereby, the rate of heat generation.

(3) The primary cooling system carries heat from the fuel assemblies.

(4) Additional cooling systems and protection barriers.

Virtually all nuclear reactors in this country are of the water-cooled variety. Basically, they all work the same way. Water enters the vessel in a closed cycle, separate from the environment, and flows through the spaces between the fuel assemblies in the fuel core. The fissioning of the fuel creates heat, which then is used to convert water in a separate system into steam. The steam is then fed to a turbine which drives a generator to produce electricity.

Increasing or decreasing the rate of fission and thus the amount of heat is accomplished by inserting or removing control rod assemblies. A reactor operator can stop the fission process by completely inserting the control rod assemblies in the reactor.

It is important to remember that the fission process in a commercial nuclear reactor can never "run away" and cause a nuclear explosion. The fuel design and the reactor system design preclude such an occurrence. It is recognized that if the primary cooling water is lost from the reactor system, it is theoretically possible that the fuel core may melt and destroy itself, but it cannot cause a nuclear explosion.

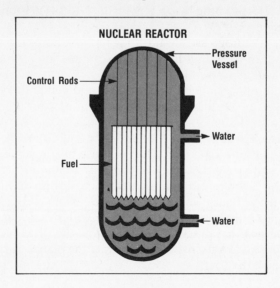

NUCLEAR REACTOR

How does a utility get a permit to build and operate a nuclear reactor?

A utility seeking to build a nuclear reactor must acquire more than two dozen permits to comply with federal, state, and regional regulations. The following paragraphs discuss only a few of the aspects related directly to nuclear matters that are reviewed by the Nuclear Regulatory Commission (NRC).

First, a construction permit must be obtained from the NRC. The utility must submit a formal application describing the design and location of the proposed plant and the safeguards to be provided. In addition, the company must show it is financially and technically qualified to build and operate such a facility.

Next, the NRC's Division of Nuclear Reactor Regulations makes the application public for consideration and intervention by interested parties. The NRC's technical experts study the application and review it with the applicant.

The application is reviewed then by the Advisory Committee on Reactor Safeguards. This committee of independent experts studies the application in detail, holds conferences with the applicant and the NRC staff, and reports its findings to the NRC and the public.

At this point, the public is afforded one of several opportunities to participate in the decision-making process. Public hearings are held by an Atomic Safety and Licensing Board near the proposed plant site, and private citizens, state and local officials, and community groups may present their views to the Board.

After hearing the testimony and reviewing all findings, the Board recommends whether a construction permit should be issued. The Board's recommendation then is reviewed by the NRC.

When a construction permit is issued, the utility may begin building the plant, subject to continuing inspection by the NRC's Division of Inspection and Enforcement.

As construction progresses—and prior to operation—the utility applies to the NRC for an operating license. The commission subjects this application to rigorous analysis and review.

In the meantime, after thorough training and comprehensive examination, employees of the utility must be licensed as plant operators by the NRC.

Further public hearings by an Atomic Safety and Licensing Board may be requested by interested persons. During these hearings, issues related to public health and safety are reviewed before an operating license is issued. Once again, the Board recommends whether the license may be issued. The NRC considers the Board's opinion and renders a final decision. An operating license is a bulky document, complete with design details and technical specifications that describe precisely how the plant was constructed and will be operated. A licensee must operate the plant in strict accordance with all details of the license.

The NRC's Division of Inspection and Enforcement has full-time resident inspectors located at each operating plant, and also performs periodic detailed inspections to assure the plants are operated safely.

How reliable are nuclear plants?

Nuclear generating stations have been very reliable producers of commercial electricity since the first practical nuclear power plant went on-line in 1957. They have been as reliable as fossil-fueled generating stations.

Oftentimes, though, when a nuclear generating station is taken off-line, it is reported in the media. It is important to note that most of the time the interruptions in service come from mechanical and other problems common to most kinds of electrical generating stations. Most often, the problems are not associated with the nuclear part of the plant.

The average availability of nuclear power stations *has* been affected when NRC directives have called for temporary shut-downs of operating plants for the installation of new equipment or modification of existing equipment. Even in 1979, when many nuclear plants were shut down by the NRC to double-check various components and add safety features, their average availability was about equal to fossil-fueled stations.

The good record of nuclear power stations is not limited to the United States but is confirmed by the operating experience of reactors around the world.

The reliability of electric generating stations is rated by the term "capacity factor." This term, expressed as a percentage, indicates how much energy was produced in a given year compared to what could have been produced if the station had run full tilt, 24 hours a day, nonstop, all year—and none are expected to run 100 percent of the time. All must be shut down on fixed schedules for maintenance and, in the case of nuclear plants, to be refueled every 12 to 18 months. A capacity factor of 65 to 70 percent is reasonable over a period of years.

Do nuclear plants affect the environment?

All methods for producing electric power affect the environment. Power plants that burn coal, oil, or natural gas emit pollutants such as sulfur and nitrogen oxides. Nuclear plants emit none of the products of combustion, because they do not "burn" anything. They do, however, emit very small amounts of radioactive materials. The combustion of coal and natural gas also results in the emission of small amounts of radioactive materials.

13

While all systems that use fuel to make energy—power plants, fireplaces, wood and coal stoves—emit some carcinogens, the amounts and risks from them are small. In study after study, no correlation has been found that links incidences of cancer with the regular operation of any electric power-producing station. It is well recognized that the number of cancers caused by other sources (smoking, diet, etc.) overwhelm the small number estimated to be caused by industrial processes in central locations where emissions are controlled. If there is a distinction between radioactivity and other potential carcinogenic materials, it is that even small quantities of radioactive emissions are much easier to measure than are small amounts of other environmental carcinogens.

The environmental problems associated with the mining and transportation necessary to make and deliver nuclear fuel are much less than with other methods of electricity production, simply because uranium contains so much energy that much less material must be mined and transported to produce the same amount of electric power.

In addition to the emissions already discussed, power plants, whether nuclear or fossil-fueled, are not able to convert all the heat energy of the fuel into electricity. This excess heat, dissipated by cooling water, is called waste heat. There are a number of ways this heat can be safely discharged.

For once-through cooling, water is pumped from an adjacent lake, river, or other body of water to cool the plant's steam condensers and absorb excess heat. Cooling water used in a nuclear power plant does not mix with the primary cooling water circuit in the reactor's core.

The cooling water is returned to its source about 15°F warmer than it was taken in. The discharge of warm water must be in accordance with state thermal discharge standards designed to protect aquatic life.

The key questions concern whether any ecological harm is done by this type of cooling system, called once-through, and if so, what can and should be done to prevent such harm?

At any power plant using water for once-through cooling, fish collect on the intake screens, which keep aquatic life and debris out of the water taken into the plant. This is called "impingement."

Aquatic organisms too small to be stopped by the screens may enter and pass through the plant's cooling system. This is called "entrainment." Organisms include bacteria, phytoplankton (aquatic plants which drift passively), zooplankton (aquatic animals which drift passively), fish eggs, larvae, and young fish. Entrainment occurs at any plant using fish-inhabited water to cool the turbine's condensers. The effect on the organisms passing through the plant may vary from one facility to another. Studies show that entrainment may not always have a significant effect on various aquatic populations.

There are a number of more costly alternatives to the once-through system of cooling condenser water.

One alternative is to build a large pond from which cooling water may be drawn and returned. Cooling ponds may also provide recreation for the public.

Another alternative is to use a somewhat smaller pond, with sprays shooting the water into the air to cool it by evaporation. The spraying of water can cause solids contained in the water to be deposited downwind. Both cooling ponds and spray ponds can cause fog and icing under certain weather conditions.

Cooling towers are another alternative. They are tall, hollow concrete structures—55 stories high and wider than the length of a football field. While cooling towers were made famous by photographs of Three Mile Island (and are often mistakenly interpreted as the reactors themselves), they—and the other methods of cooling discussed here—are common to large coal, gas, and oil-fired electric generating stations.

The hollow cooling towers work on the principle of a natural draft and evaporation to cool the heated water from the generating system. Again, none of the primary water that is in the isolated reactor cooling circuit ever flows through the cooling tower, so there is no possibility of radioactive materials being released to the environment through a plant's waste heat disposal system.

With cooling towers, no significant amount of warm water or heat is added to any natural body of water. Studies indicate there is very little possibility of adverse environmental effects from cooling towers.

NUCLEAR POWER IS SAFE

Nothing is completely risk-free, including a nuclear reactor.

Radioactivity in extremely large amounts can cause injury or death. (See "What is radiation sickness?") Nuclear materials and processes, therefore, are painstakingly isolated from the public through good design, engineering operations, and monitoring.

In generating the large amounts of electricity society requires, all systems release some pollutants and cause some risks to miners, workers, transportation personnel, and the public. However, engineering and control to reduce risks to acceptable levels make a system viable.

Commercial nuclear energy boasts a remarkable safety record, because safety considerations are a paramount concern from the time a utility decides it needs a new plant, through its construction and operational life, and eventual decommissioning.

What kind of safety analysis is done for nuclear plants?

When an electric company applies to the NRC for a permit to construct a nuclear power plant, among the studies it must submit are a Preliminary Safety Analysis Report (PSAR) and a detailed Environmental Impact Statement (EIS). The PSAR evaluates myriad safety and protection designs and feature design details, as well as information relating to the site. The PSAR and EIS include data on:

15

- meteorological, hydrological, geological, seismological, and environmental aspects of the site
- the reactor
- the coolant system
- containment
- the emergency core cooling system
- instrumentation and control
- electrical power systems
- radioactive waste systems
- auxiliary systems
- power conversion systems
- plant structures and shielding
- accident analysis

Before a PSAR is completed, behavior of each of these systems and components is analyzed under accident conditions to assure the integrity of the designs and the safety of the plant. This arduous review procedure, taking up to two years or more, must be completed before a construction permit can be issued.

The Final Safety Analysis Report (FSAR) treats such subjects as the operation and maintenance of the plant, including its organization for operations and staffing.

How are reactors made safe?

Reactors are made safe through well-established designs, careful engineering, and exhaustive operator training. Designers make use of the multiple barrier concept (using many barriers instead of one) and redundancy designs (providing several back-up barriers to accomplish the same task) to provide "defense in depth."

The multiple barrier concept is achieved by keeping virtually all of the radioactive fission products trapped within the solid fuel pellets, within the fuel rod's metal cladding, within the reactor's steel vessel and primary system, and within the reinforced concrete and steel containment buildings. These multiple barriers prevent fission products from reaching the public.

The redundancy design concept means a nuclear power plant has so many overlapping safety features that if, for any reason, several should fail, there still would be sufficient additional barriers and systems to provide safety.

During normal operation, the reactor control system adjusts the reactor output by changing the position of control rods that absorb the atom-splitting neutrons. In the event of an abnormal occurrence, the reactor is shut down automatically by a protection system that causes all the control rods to be inserted into the reactor core, immediately stopping the chain reaction.

To guard against the remote possibility of loss of reactor cooling water, the reactor system is equipped with an emergency core cooling system

(ECCS), designed to force reserve water into the reactor automatically if the reactor coolant pressure drops to a predetermined level.

What are some of the specific safety devices?

A number of safety devices and barriers prevent the release of radioactive materials.

- The fuel itself is made of dense ceramic pellets, which contain the uranium and the radioactive waste materials resulting from fission.
- The pellets are sealed within metal tubes, called cladding.
- The reactor is in a thick steel pressure vessel, which contains the core with the tubes holding the nuclear fuel and the control rods and the primary coolant.
- Each reactor is encircled by a concrete wall, which supports the vessel and provides a shield against radiation.
- A leak-tight steel shell also encloses the reactor and houses all the reactor system components. The steel shell is designed to prevent the escape of radioactive materials from the containment building in the event of an emergency.
- A massive outer concrete wall acts as another radiation shield. This outer wall—the one visitors see—is the domed building that houses many reactor units.
- An emergency core cooling system ensures that a back-up supply of water will prevent the reactor core from over-heating if the primary coolant water supply should be reduced.
- The reactor is remotely operated from a central control room located in a different part of the plant. In addition to its human operators, the reactor has automatic controls to shut it down if changes from normal operating conditions are sensed. The control rods governing the amount of heat produced by the reactor can be used to shut down the reactor by either human or automatic direction.
- Auxiliary controls on new plants make it possible to shut down the reactors manually from outside the central control room should the central control room become unusable.

In addition to these barriers and controls, several systems are built into a nuclear power plant to trap potentially harmful amounts of radioactive material and help prevent them from being released to the outside environment. Filters, evaporators, and other equipment remove almost all of the radioactive materials and allow them to be isolated and disposed of safely. Tiny amounts of radioactive material are released in a controlled manner only where there is assurance that the level of material released is in compliance with the strict standards set by federal authorities.

Monitoring for ambient radioactivity continues around the clock. Samples of air, soil, water, vegetation, fish, crops, milk, etc. are taken for analysis periodically. Radiological monitoring is often checked by independent specialists hired by the utility.

Nuclear plant monitoring is reviewed on a continuing basis by inspectors from NRC's Division of Inspection and Enforcement. State agencies, in many cases, also take samples and compare results with those obtained by the plant operator. The U.S. Public Health Service also makes special surveys around nuclear power plants.

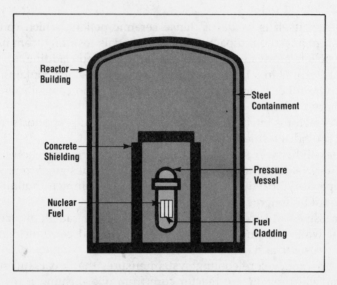

Reactor Building

Steel Containment

Concrete Shielding

Pressure Vessel

Nuclear Fuel

Fuel Cladding

Could an earthquake destroy a nuclear plant?

As has been noted, nuclear plants are massive structures, built to resist earthquakes and other natural calamities.

Before a construction site for a nuclear plant is approved, it is studied for any geological indications of earthquakes as a potentially destructive threat in the area. The NRC permits nuclear plant construction only after satisfactory design criteria have been defined.

Moreover, nuclear power plants are designed specifically to withstand an earthquake. Each plant must be able to withstand the maximum earthquake motion that could be expected at its site and be able to shut down safely. Unlike fossil plants, which are not designed to the same exacting standards for earthquake resistance, nuclear plants can be expected to continue operating during a moderate earthquake.

Nuclear plants in California and Japan have withstood earthquakes of magnitudes as great as 6.5 on the Richter scale. Earthquake standards for nuclear plant construction are several times more stringent than for hospitals, apartment buildings, and other structures, where an earthquake could cause immediate injuries to the public.

What, then, are the risks of nuclear power operations?

Dr. Bernard L. Cohen, professor of physics at the University of Pittsburgh, has thoroughly investigated this subject. Writing in *Consumers' Re-*

search Magazine about a scientific paper he had written earlier for *Health Physics*, Dr. Cohen explained:

"We collected quantitative information on risks from a wide variety of sources and analyzed it in terms of life expectancy reduction . . . the average amount one's life is shortened by each risk. . . . In spite of all the publicity about dangers of nuclear energy . . . a typical estimated Life Expectancy Reduction if all U.S. electricity were nuclear is .03 days. For reactor accidents the critics estimate . . . two days while government-sponsored scientists estimate only .02 days, so even if we accept the former, the total Life Expectancy Reduction from a full nuclear energy program would be just over two days."

By contrast, cigarette smoking reduces life expectancy 1,600 days; being overweight, 900 days; motor vehicle accidents, 200 days; mining and construction work due to accidents only, 300 days.

Dr. Cohen added:

"As an extension of worries about air pollution and degradation of the environment by prodigious use of energy, some people claim that there are great environmental risks in our general acceptance of technology. A simple test of this viewpoint is the correlation between the life expectancy in various nations and their technological development. In countries with advanced technology, such as the United States, Western Europe, Australia, and Japan, life expectancy is about 71 years. Life expectancy in a sample of other countries is 68 years in Poland and Rumania, 61 years in Mexico, 55 years in Turkey, 45 years in India, and 32 years in Chad and Ivory Coast. The correlation with technological development is clear, and the complete list strongly reinforces that conclusion. We may infer that technological development brings us about 30 years of increased life expectancy."

How are the plants regulated during operation?

Throughout the life of a plant, inspectors from the NRC's Division of Inspection and Enforcement make frequent announced and unannounced, day and night inspection visits at random intervals. They make sure the plant is being operated and maintained in accordance with safety standards and the provisions of the operating license.

The federal government requires that plants be checked for radioactive effluents, among many other specifics, and that findings be reported to the appropriate agencies. State agencies perform similar monitoring. In addition, these agencies require written reports from utilities on any changes in conditions or operations.

Can a reactor explode?

It is physically impossible for a commercial nuclear reactor to explode like an atomic bomb, whether through accident, sabotage or any other reason.

Yet, in a 1980 survey, pollsters found that only one in three people were aware of this.

There are several differences between nuclear energy used for electricity production and for weapons. The nature, purity, arrangement, and concentration of nuclear materials in an atomic bomb is significantly different from that in a nuclear reactor.

In addition to differences in materials, atomic bombs require that these nuclear materials be brought together rapidly, almost instantaneously, into a precise, compact shape. Commercial reactor fuel can *never* be rearranged so the material would be able to undergo a nuclear explosion. Under any circumstances, a commercial reactor can only release nuclear energy slowly.

The difference between commercial nuclear reactors and atomic bombs can be illustrated by an analogy comparing the relationship between uranium and nuclear energy with the relationship between grain and bread. Every year at harvest time, there are numerous reports of explosions—often deaths—in grain silos. These explosions are a result of the chemical energy in the grain being released suddenly when a spark ignites an area full of fine grain dust. That same chemical energy in the grain, once it has been made into bread, can be released slowly by the human digestion process. Nothing can be done to this new chemical and physical arrangement of grain—the bread—to make it explode. In the same way, atomic weapons and nuclear reactors use similar starting material—uranium. However, a commercial reactor can release its energy only slowly and can no more explode like a bomb than can a loaf of bread.

What about the possibility of a hydrogen bubble explosion at Three Mile Island?

During the March 1979 accident at the Three Mile Island Unit 2 reactor, there was considerable concern, following speculation by a few people in the NRC and subsequent press reports, that a hydrogen bubble in the reactor vessel might explode. The fact is that it was physically impossible all along for the hydrogen bubble to explode.

Hydrogen, generated from chemical reactions between the overheated reactor's fuel cladding and water, was trapped in a bubble in the reactor vessel. However, hydrogen, like anything combustible, needs oxygen to burn or explode. There was no oxygen in the reactor vessel and no possible source of oxygen. Thus, the hydrogen could not explode, or even burn.

Some confusion arose over the fact that as the hydrogen leaked out of the reactor into the large concrete containment building, it did burn, and a small explosion did take place—not in the reactor but in the containment building. This small explosion in no way affected the strength of the reinforced concrete containment building, because it was designed to take pressure increases of the type experienced.

The Technical Task Force of the Presidential Commission on the Accident at Three Mile Island—the Kemeny Commission—along with many other

20

subsequent studies, examined the technical details of the accident, and concluded:

"No explosion was possible within the reactor vessel at any time."

It also concluded:

"In spite of the impossibility of a hydrogen explosion within the reactor vessel, the Nuclear Regulatory Commission was greatly concerned about such an explosion from March 30 until April 2, 1979."

On April 10, 1979, then-NRC Chairman Joseph M. Hendrie, testifying before the Senate Subcommittee on Nuclear Regulation, told Senator Pete Domenici:

"The possibility of a flammable mixture turns out to have been a misplaced concern."

Hendrie explained that it took the NRC several days before its analyses showed "there hadn't been any oxygen involved, or very little, if any."

What is a nuclear meltdown—a China syndrome?

Even after a nuclear reactor is shut down and all fissioning stops, the core remains quite hot due to decay heat. Decay heat is analogous to hot ashes after a fire has been put out. It is so called, because it decays away; i.e., the fuel cools off over a period of time. About 80 percent of the decay heat is gone within an hour, and some 85 percent dissipates within a week after shut-down.

However, during the first few hours after a reactor is shut down, the fuel must be kept cool so decay heat will not overheat the core and possibly lead to melting of some or large amounts of the fuel.

Under worst-case assumptions of failure of all cooling systems in a reactor accident, it is theoretically possible that the decay heat could cause the core temperature to exceed the 5000° F melting point of the fuel. The melting of some or all of the more than 100 tons of fuel in the core is called a "meltdown." Concern that the molten fuel could melt its way through the reactor vessel and reinforced concrete containment building and into the ground has been coined, facetiously, a "China syndrome" as a child might dig a hole "clear to China."

The possibility and consequences of melting some of a commercial reactor's core have been studied extensively through models, because no commercial-type reactor has suffered a meltdown.

With respect to Three Mile Island, the Technical Assessment Task Force for the President's Commission on the accident pointed out that even if major fuel melting had occurred (which was not the case), it would require at least three days for the molten uranium to penetrate the 15-foot thick reinforced concrete floor. The commission also estimated the molten uranium would mix with and thus be cooled by the concrete and would solidify in one or two days, long before it could melt through the floor.

Indeed, when every imaginable worst-case scenario is drawn up to discuss a meltdown, it ignores the simple fact that the reactor building and systems contain millions of gallons of water, which would be used to cool the uranium.

While core melting would be a very serious accident, it could not result in a nuclear-type explosion and widespread death as some imaginative works of fiction have suggested.

RADIATION AND RADIOACTIVITY

People have been exposed to radiation from the beginning of time.

Radioactivity is in the air we breathe, the food we eat, the water we drink, the homes we live in, and the earth we walk on. Even our bodies are mildly radioactive, and always have been.

The radiation from the operation of a nuclear plant is no different physically than our natural "background" radiation. It consists of a stream of particles or rays that come from unstable atoms.

There are essentially three types of radiation: alpha and beta particles and gamma rays. Alpha particles travel about an inch in the air and can be stopped by sheets of paper. Beta particles travel a few feet in the air and can be stopped by an inch of wood. Gamma rays travel a greater distance but can be stopped by dense shielding material, such as lead or concrete.

Radiation occurs in a nuclear reactor when a uranium atom is split in the fission process. The resulting fission fragments, or lighter weight atoms, are generally unstable.

Unstable atoms cannot exist in nature forever. They become stable by emitting energy (radiation) over a period of time, which can vary from fractions of a second to thousands of years, depending upon the specific type of atom involved.

Mankind uses radiation to perform many functions. For example, X-rays are man-made radiation used to reveal tooth decay, broken bones, tumors, and details of wounds to assist in medical treatment. Radiation also is widely used by the medical profession to kill cancer cells.

How are radioactivity and radiation measured?

Units of radioactivity are measured in curies—after Madame Marie Curie, who discovered several radioactive elements. One curie is a measurement of the amount of radioactivity generally associated with one gram of radium. A picocurie—one thousandth of a millionth of a curie—is the unit used in discussing small amounts of radioactivity in the environment.

Other terms are used to describe the absorption of radiation into the body and the effects it might have. For a loose parallel, consider that food has a calorie (energy) content. When it is absorbed into the body, it is measured as fat. Beyond that, still another measurement is used to describe the biological effect: stress on the heart.

In discussing radiation, a rad is the physical measurement of the energy-ionizing radiation deposits in tissue. This term is seldom heard in public discussions, however.

22

A rem is the measurement of the biological effects.

Unlike discussing body fats, which subsequently are broken down into still other measurements such as cholesterol, the term rem itself accounts for the different effects on living tissue from absorption of different types of radiation. There are, however, subdivisions for rad and rem. A millirad (mrad) is 1/1000 of a rad; a millirem (mrem) is 1/1000 of a rem. Both units are used in discussing low levels of radiation. Millirem is the term most frequently used in public discussions, because the amounts being discussed are so small.

A U.S. citizen is estimated to receive an average total of 100 to 200 millirems of low-level radiation exposure each year. Over half the radiation to which the population is exposed comes from the natural background radiation from such sources as the sun, outer space, the earth, the atmosphere and our own bodies. The other portion comes from man-made sources of radiation such as X-ray units.

Many activities in which we regularly engage increase our yearly dosages of radiation. We receive man-made radiation from coast-to-coast jet flights, from various consumer products such as smoke detectors, color television sets, and luminous dial clocks, and medical X-rays. Crews of high-altitude commercial jet airliners receive an additional occupational radiation exposure from cosmic rays in the range of 300–400 millirems per year.

Coal-fired electric power plants emit measurable amounts of radioactivity, due to the presence of naturally radioactive materials in coal. Geothermal power plants emit radioactivity, too, due to the presence of radon, a radioactive gas, in the steam. Wood stoves emit some radioactivity. Nuclear power plants emit some radioactivity to the environment, but only a very small percentage of the radiation to which we are exposed from all other sources.

For 1980, nuclear energy's contribution to the total estimated U.S. collective dose (not including occupational doses) was slightly more than one tenth of one percent. The typical neighbor of a modern nuclear plant will receive radiation exposure of less than one millirem a year added to his or her average natural background level. Without electricity from nuclear plants, the typical American is likely to be exposed to about 150 millirems of radiation annually, not accounting for radiation from whatever alternative sources of energy are used to fill the gap. With nuclear energy, the 150 millirems becomes about 150.3 millirems.

What is radiation sickness? Can it be treated?

Overexposure to radiation, either as one massive dose or as substantial amounts over a period of time—hundreds and thousands of times greater than natural background radiation—can cause radiation sickness. The illness results primarily from injury to the body's ability to produce blood cells. It can be treated successfully depending on the exposure.

Anyone exposed to an inappropriate amount of radiation would be treated or at least placed under observation. Symptoms of radiation sickness typically begin to appear with doses of 200,000 to 600,000 millirems. An exposure of 600,000 millirems left untreated could be fatal. For perspective, recall that people living near nuclear power plants may receive about 0.3 millirems annually in addition to normal background radiation of about 150 millirems; 200 millirems, if medical X-rays are included in calculating the average. Thus, 200,000 millirems is 666,666 times greater than that received by the nuclear plant neighbor.

Radiation sickness may be treated by bone marrow transfusions, cleansing of the blood, drugs, and other known and familiar procedures. It should not be confused with cancer, which is one possible effect of exposure to radiation, although the risk of cancer decreases proportionately with the decrease in radiation exposure level.

It should be noted that all of the talk about radiation dangers has left the false impression that exposure at any level is permanently harmful. The truth is that radiation sickness has been treated successfully. In addition, it is well recognized that extremely high levels of radiation are used in treating cancer. The lurid association is often made between radiation and the immediate injuries to victims at Hiroshima and Nagasaki. Those injuries were the result of the blast and fire from detonation of atomic weapons. Since nuclear plants cannot explode like a bomb, such injuries cannot be associated with nuclear power plant accidents.

Who decides on radiation protection standards?

The Environmental Protection Agency (EPA) sets radiation control guidelines to protect the environment, the public, and workers in the nuclear industry. The Nuclear Regulatory Commission (NRC) is responsible for regulatory application of these guidelines and for the implementation and enforcement of radiation exposure controls in nuclear power plants.

Present radiation standards have evolved from more than 50 years' study of the biological effects of radiation, and recommendations for exposure control by radiation protection organizations, which include physicians, radiobiologists, and other scientists. Much of this effort was completed before nuclear power plants were built, because there are many other natural and medical sources of radiation.

In 1928, the International Society of Radiology sponsored formation of the International Commission on Radiation Protection. A year after, the U.S. National Council on Radiation Protection and Measurements was organized. Both organizations continue to propose radiation protection controls.

Independent reviews of radiation guidelines are conducted periodically by the National Academy of Sciences' National Research Council through the Committee on the Biological Effects of Ionizing Radiation. An international audit is provided by the United Nations Scientific Committee on the

Effects of Atomic Radiation. The National Academy of Sciences committee issued its most recent report with specific recommendations in 1980.

Radiation protection for X-rays was proposed as early as 1901, and standards for controlling radiation from such medical sources as X-rays and radium were established as far back as the 1930s. Radiation control, then, has been studied continuously for more than five decades and unites the collective experience and judgment of the world's experts. Because their work is under constant study and improvement, today's standards represent a consensus unequaled in any other field of environmental protection.

How much radioactivity is released from a nuclear power plant?

The Environmental Protection Agency (EPA), in the booklet *Questions and Answers About Nuclear Power Plants,* has answered this question as follows:

"The concentration of radioactive materials released to the environment is very low—often so low that it is difficult to detect. Most radiation we encounter in our daily lives comes from natural sources—in our foods, in rocks, in the earth, in the air, and in the water—and—for the average person—is approximately 130 millirems a year. . . . Little can be done to remove this radiation; it has been around since the world began. Other radiation is man-made; the greatest amount comes from X-rays used in medical and dental diagnosis and therapy. Another source of radiation exposure is fallout from former atmospheric weapons testing, which accounts for about 15 millirems per person per year. Radiation from jet flights, radioactive luminous watch dials, and color television add about 2 millirems per year. By contrast, emissions from nuclear power plants and other atomic facilities average an annual exposure of only a fraction of a millirem per person. The average annual exposure of people living within a 50-mile radius of nuclear stations is less than a millirem."

In the year 2000, assuming nuclear energy provides about one-third of the nation's electricity, the average citizen will receive an estimated yearly dose of less than one millirem from nuclear energy. This average will not increase no matter how much of the world's electricity is generated by nuclear power plants.

A former Atomic Energy Commissioner, Clarence E. Larson, put things in perspective when he said:

"A person living every minute at the boundary of one of our licensed nuclear plants—drinking the discharge water, breathing the air, and eating fish from the same water—would have to remain there for more than 200 years to get the same radiation exposure effects as will result from a single chest X-ray."

How much exposure do workers in nuclear power receive?

Workers in the commercial nuclear industry necessarily receive more radiation than do members of the public. Of the 45,978 radiation workers in 1978, 65 percent received radiation doses that were too small to measure. While the exposure level for workers is higher than the natural background level, it is still many times less than levels at which any observable medical effects occur.

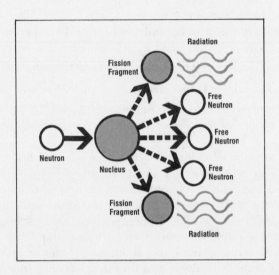

If small amounts of long-lived radioactive materials are released to the environment, is there a buildup to dangerous levels over a long period of time?

All radioactive materials decay and eventually become non-radioactive. This process can take anywhere from fractions of seconds to thousands of years.

The natural background radiation of the Earth comes from a variety of radioactive materials that may take days or billions of years to decay. The presence of this background radiation often makes it impossible to detect very small additions from human activities, such as commercial nuclear power.

Commercial nuclear stations and facilities emit small quantities of more than a dozen different radioactive materials. Most have life-spans measured in minutes or hours, and only four last for long periods. These four are radioactive forms of hydrogen, carbon, krypton, and iodine. The specific radioactivity of these four long-lived materials is very low, but they require from decades to hundreds and even thousands of years to decay.

The Organization for Economic Co-Operation and Development's Nuclear Energy Agency, representing some 25 countries, recently studied the long-term environmental effects of these regular releases. The study concluded that even when it is assumed there is a nuclear industry with many times more reactors than exist today, the greatest population exposures

FROM NATURAL BACKGROUND RADIATION:
(millirem/year)*

From cosmic rays –35

From air –5

From building materials –34

From food –25

From ground –11

FROM THREE MILE ISLAND ACCIDENT—1

FROM MAN-MADE SOURCES RADIATION:
(millirem/year)*

From coast-to-coast jet flight –5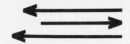

From color television –1

From one chest X ray –50

*From living within a 50-mile radius
of a nuclear power plant –0.001*

*One millirem per year is equal to: moving to an elevation 100 feet
higher; increasing your diet by 4%; watching one additional hour of
black-and-white TV per day; taking a 4-5 day vacation in the Sierra
Nevada Mountains. (Source: Atomic Industrial Forum)

over long periods of time (500 years) would be at worst only a few percent of natural background radiation, typically just fractions of a percent.

While the effects of tiny amounts of radiation are not known, and may never be known precisely, scientists agree that a buildup of man-made radioactivity amounting to only a fraction of a percent of natural radioactivity cannot present a significant hazard.

Why is any release of radioactivity permitted?

It is impossible to have zero releases from nuclear plants, just as it is impossible to have zero release of pollutants from any industrial process or from nature itself. What is done with commercial nuclear power is to assure that any releases are well below the levels for significant environmental or human health effects. This practice has been observed in the nuclear power industry from its inception. Releases of radioactivity from nuclear power plants to the environment are limited, therefore, to amounts that will not present an undue hazard to public health.

Do radiation protection standards take into account the cumulative effect of several reactors on one site and of multiple plant sites in one region?

The Nuclear Regulatory Commission (NRC) has always considered multiple sources of radiation in protecting the public. A plant's design criteria must take into account the release of radioactive effluents on a cumulative basis.

Radioactive releases during the operation of each nuclear reactor at the same site must be kept as low as reasonably achievable, as defined by the NRC, and maximums for the site or individual plants cannot be exceeded.

Similar attention is given to the cumulative effect of nuclear power facilities at other sites throughout a given geographical area. NRC regulations provide that the average radiation exposure of the public due to the operation of *all* nuclear plants will continue to be less than one percent of the average natural background radiation.

Has any person in the United States ever been exposed to an overdose of radiation from commercial nuclear power plants?

No member of the U.S. public has ever been exposed to radiation levels above the standards set by the government.

Rare cases of researchers and workers being overexposed have occurred, mostly in the early days of nuclear science. Workers in commercial nuclear power production are protected by extensive precautions to prevent repeated overexposure. Some workers have been exposed accidentally to radiation in excess of regulatory standards, but not to an extent that could be considered dangerous.

The entire industrial and commercial radiation-related industry is remarkable, even to insurance companies, for the small number of overexposures. Since 1940, there have been far fewer than 100 accidents *worldwide* in which anyone has been injured by accidental exposure to radiation. None of these occurred at nuclear power plants or as a result of nuclear power plant operations.

Were people overexposed at Three Mile Island?

The maximum exposure of any member of the *local* public as a consequence of the accident at Three Mile Island was less than a small fraction of one percent of the amount of radiation that people living in Harrisburg, Pennsylvania receive year-round from natural sources. Furthermore, this maximum theoretical dose from the accident is much less than that allowed by federal standards for members of the public.

As for the 2 million persons *living within 50 miles* of Three Mile Island, the average radiation exposure was a small fraction of one percent of normal, annual background radiation exposure. This amount is less than the additional background radiation a resident of Denver receives every week compared with a city of lower elevation, such as Boston or Harrisburg.

These estimates and conclusions have been verified repeatedly by government, industry, and independent studies. A General Accounting Office report to the Congress, titled "Three Mile Island: The Most Studied Nuclear Accident in History," confirmed these conclusions with respect to radiation exposure.

THE THREE MILE ISLAND ACCIDENT

On Wednesday, March 28, 1979, at 4:00 a.m., in the Unit 2 nuclear power plant on Three Mile Island near Harrisburg, Pennsylvania, a series of events resulting from equipment failure, inappropriate procedures, and operator confusion all combined to escalate what could have been an easily corrected problem into an international sensation. Despite the absence of operator or public injury, the accident created the worst crisis ever faced by the commercial nuclear industry.

Very simply, the Three Mile Island reactor gradually lost some of the cooling water that is pumped through its core. This caused the reactor to shut itself down, but the leak eventually left insufficient water to remove all of the core's residual decay heat. When the level of water in the core became low enough, the upper portion of the core was uncovered. The temperature began to rise, allowing the metal cladding of the fuel rods to overheat and react chemically with the water. This caused a small quantity of radioactive material to be released from the damaged fuel into the reactor's cooling water circuit.

The reactor's core remained partially uncovered and inadequately cooled for several hours until operators were able to determine the nature of the problem and fill the core once again, leaving a seriously damaged core cooling under water.

Will there be unpredictable long-term health effects from the Three Mile Island accident?

No. The maximum radiation release (see "Were people overexposed at Three Mile Island?") was only a small fraction of the radiation exposure everyone receives continuously from nature.

The President's Commission on the Accident at Three Mile Island concluded: "On the basis of present scientific knowledge, the radiation doses received by the general population as a result of exposure to the radioactivity released during the accident were so small that there will be no detectable additional cases of cancer, developmental abnormalities, or genetic ill-health as a consequence of the accident at TMI."

What lessons were learned from Three Mile Island?

Although the construction and safety features of the reactor system worked as designed to prevent catastrophe, weaknesses were revealed. In spite of many shocks, problems, and confusion, the reactor systems contained the accident. Every industry and government study confirms there was never a serious danger to the public.

Since the earliest days of the commercial nuclear industry, nuclear power stations have been designed with multiple layers of safety. Thus, despite equipment failure, misleading information, and operator confusion, this "defense in depth" concept contained the accident and protected the public.

The accident, nonetheless, was serious and clearly a catastrophe for the reactor's owners. It presented the commercial nuclear industry with the greatest financial problem in its history.

Some of the most important lessons learned were:

1. Reactor operator training needed to be upgraded.

This has been accomplished with more exhaustive training programs, through the use of simulators (similar to those airplane pilots use) and through the guiding efforts of the Institute of Nuclear Power Operations (INPO). With all nuclear-operating utilities as members, INPO is focusing on the establishment of benchmarks of excellence for the operation of nuclear power plants. It was organized by utilities in direct response to the Three Mile Island accident.

INPO represents a new approach for the electric utility industry. Its objective of industry self-improvement draws on 25 years of reliable operating experience. INPO's philosophy of helping utilities help themselves recognizes that resolving an operating problem at one nuclear plant can help avoid a similar problem at many other plants.

2. Regulatory practices and procedures needed overhauling.

This has been and undoubtedly will continue to be the source of considerable attention and debate. The development of new and improved operating procedures requires imagination and flexibility from operators and regulators, rather than the emphasis on sterile procedural requirements, which was the rule in the past.

3. Increased and improved technical communications are needed between reactor owners and operators.

To this end, the Electric Power Research Institute (EPRI) set up a separate division called the Nuclear Safety Analysis Center (NSAC) to scrutinize all technical factors surrounding the accident at TMI; to identify improvements; to assist General Public Utilities, the owner of the Three Mile Island plant, in the recovery; to develop recommendations for practical improvements in reactor safety; and to serve as an information exchange for utilities, reactor supplier groups, and the NRC. (General Public Utilities Corp. is a holding company. Its subsidiary, Metropolitan Edison Company, serves the territory around the plant and operated the reactor.)

4. Nuclear electricity is less expensive than most alternatives, but accidents can be very expensive.

The cost of replacement power to Metropolitan Edison and its customers amounts to nearly $1 million a day as long as TMI-2 and the undamaged TMI-1 are shut down. The fuel-related cost of replacement coal-based electricity is nearly twice that produced by TMI; for replacement oil-based electricity, it is five to ten times greater.

The total cost to replace the less expensive nuclear electricity with that from other fuels, combined with the costs to clean up the accident, may well exceed $1 billion, allowing for inflation. For the future, the industry has established a mutual insurance plan to provide utilities with an indemnity payment to cover part of the cost of replacement power in the event a plant is shut down for an extended period of time following an accident. The plan also established a vehicle to provide increased insurance coverage for the costs of future accidents.

5. Better emergency communications are needed.

Special telephone lines have been established between nuclear utilities and their reactor suppliers to make use of the suppliers' extensive engineering knowledge of reactor design and nuclear systems. Direct lines also link the utilities with the NRC, and in an emergency, assistance may be obtained quickly from experts in many fields, who are available on call through lists established by the Emergency Preparedness Division of INPO. Public information procedures have been revamped to keep the public accurately and fully informed during future incidents, thus avoiding the mass confusion that occurred at TMI.

Has the nuclear industry made reactors safer since Three Mile Island?

Yes. The United States electric power industry has responded quickly and forcefully to the accident by revising procedures and training in nuclear power stations, making equipment changes, and establishing major new organizations whose jobs are to correct inadequacies shown up by the accident. As a result, nuclear power stations are even safer today than they were in March 1979.

The nuclear industry has effected many specific changes to improve safety. These include:

— more instruments to monitor reactor system conditions and let operators know at a glance trends in reactor conditions;
— greater use of past experience with improved technical communication;
— expanded training requirements, more stringent testing, and extensive use of simulators for operators, under the guidance and standards established by the Institute of Nuclear Power Operations (INPO);
— modifications based on the human engineering of controls and the control room;
— direct communications between the control room, the Nuclear Regulatory Commission, and the reactor's designers and builders;
— the establishment of on-site support centers to coordinate the work of auxiliary operators and other technical personnel without interfering with the control room, and where they can have access to plans and drawings of the plant and other essential records; and
— changes to the containment buildings to better prepare them for emergencies, such as new radiation monitoring and water level instruments as well as facilities for easily extracting samples of reactor coolant water and containment air for radioactivity analysis.

How are they going to clean up Three Mile Island?

The accident left large volumes of liquid and gaseous radioactive wastes in the TMI buildings and water and air contaminated with radioactive materials from the damaged core.

The gaseous waste trapped in the containment building was essentially krypton-85, a gas used medically to perform lung scans to ascertain lung function and health. Because krypton is a chemically inert gas, it cannot concentrate in the biological or environmental food chains.

After nine months of debate over the health hazards of this krypton gas, Metropolitan Edison was authorized to vent the gas into the atmosphere. This resulted in a maximum total additional off-site radiation exposure of 0.02 millirem—less than the radiation dose a person receives from the radioactivity in natural gas in an average day's cooking with a household gas range.

Several systems will be required to clean the contaminated water, two of which have already been installed and are now processing water that contains material with low and medium levels of radioactivity. These systems work in much the same way as home water softeners, removing the undesirable materials to leave purified water. Currently, this purified water is stored at the site in large tanks.

After the water has been cleansed of radioactive materials, the task of decontaminating floors, pipe surfaces, etc., will begin. Decontamination of radioactively contaminated surfaces is a relatively straightforward process, consisting principally of hands-on scrubbing with water, detergents, and treated cloths.

By January 1981, virtually all of the 500,000 gallons of radioactive water in the auxiliary building had been decontaminated. Most of the building also had been decontaminated to the extent that all areas were accessible. The low-level radioactive wastes from this decontamination are being stored temporarily on-site.

The next step in the clean-up process will be decontamination of the 700,000 gallons of radioactive water in the containment building, decontamination of the interior surfaces in the building, and removal and disposal of the damaged core. The entire process is estimated to take at least another four years; proceedings are moving cautiously to accommodate public hearings, NRC studies, and scientific scrutiny to learn more about the accident and its causes and effects to assure there is no risk to public health and safety.

Could a Three Mile Island type of accident happen again?

It is unlikely an accident like the one that occurred on Three Mile Island will happen again. Significant physical, procedural, and organizational safety precautions have been taken to prevent that specific type of accident.

However, this does not mean that utilities operating nuclear stations believe accidents cannot occur. All of the multiple safety systems and organizational precautions are put in place because engineers and scientists must assume that accidents will occur. The reactor stations are designed and built and operators are trained to deal with accidents so that the design, construction, and operation of nuclear power stations do not endanger the public health and safety.

The fact is that no member of the public suffered physical harm from the accident at Three Mile Island. Both the NRC and the utility met the primary requirement of safe operation—protecting the public. The industry and NRC have further improved reactor safety and have greatly reduced the likelihood of another accident.

What about insurance protection against losses that might result from a nuclear accident?

Under the Price-Anderson Act, a federal law, each nuclear reactor owner must carry at least $560 million worth of liability insurance. This consists of $160 million of liability insurance purchasable from insurance pools (up from $60 million at the inception of Price-Anderson); $370 million currently available from assessments of $5 million per operating reactor, paid by the utilities; and $30 million under the Price-Anderson government indemnity program. As the number of operating reactors grows, the government indemnity program will be phased out, and the amount available to persons who might be injured will increase beyond the existing $560 million ceiling.

The purpose of the governmental indemnity program is not so much to protect utilities from liability as to assure the public of prompt and adequate compensation in the case of an extremely unlikely event that might exceed the financial resources of the nuclear plant owner.

Most homeowner insurance policies contain a nuclear exclusion clause, just as there are exclusions for earthquakes, floods, landslides, and other natural disasters. However, the Price-Anderson Act protects homeowners against the financial consequences of a nuclear accident without direct cost.

To receive compensation under the no-fault provisions of the Act, anyone filing a claim has only to demonstrate the amount of the damages and to show they resulted from "an extraordinary nuclear occurrence." Thus, the nuclear exclusion clauses in homeowners' policies channel coverage into nuclear insurance pools without homeowners or other private parties paying any premiums; only the utilities pay them.

Private insurance companies supply the required liability insurance for all nuclear facilities that could cause damage to private property. The coverage (for liability plus property loss to the insured) provided by these insurance pools is the greatest commitment insurers have ever made—a measure of confidence in the nuclear industry.

Even though there was no damage to off-site property from Three Mile Island, homeowners who elected to evacuate were compensated liberally by the utility's insurers. A total of $1,213,000 was paid immediately after the accident to homeowners who elected to evacuate.

Based on nuclear plants' excellent safety record, the insurance companies have refunded about $11.6 million of premiums. For that portion of the nuclear indemnity provided through the federal government, utilities pay about $90,000 annually for a 1000-megawatt power station. So far, utilities have paid the government more than $10 million for this protection and none has been paid out.

According to the insurance organizations, nuclear facility operators have established a safety record that may be unmatched in American industry, even including the TMI accident.

DISPOSING OF SPENT NUCLEAR FUEL

When oil, coal, or gas are burned, nothing is left to be reused as fuel. But part of a reactor's fuel can be recycled and used again.

The core of nuclear fuel in the reactor consists of many individual fuel assemblies. One-fourth to one-third of the fuel assemblies are replaced about once a year. The used or "spent fuel" assemblies are stored temporarily in a specially constructed water pool at the power plant site.

During the first several months, much of the short-lived radioactivity decays and is gone. In fact, 98 percent is gone within six months. The water in the pools is a shield against radiation and the spent fuel gives the water a faint blue glow.

Approximately one-fourth of the uranium-235 in the original reactor fuel is still usable, along with an equivalent amount of recoverable plutonium which also can be used as reactor fuel. Thus, the energy value of the fissionable materials in the spent fuel when removed from the reactor is about one-half the energy value of the fuel when first placed in the reactor. Fuel bundles are removed while there is still usable fuel left in them because as waste products build up from the fission process they dampen the nuclear chain reaction and prevent full use of the depleting fissionable materials.

All the spent fuel from nuclear power plants in this country during the remainder of this century could be stored safely in a water-cooled basin smaller in area than the reflecting pool between the Washington Monument and the Lincoln Memorial in Washington, DC.

The potential energy value of the usable uranium and plutonium within the spent fuel can be equated to the energy value of petroleum used to make electricity. The recoverable energy from the spent fuel that will be accumulated by the end of the century is equivalent to over 10 billion barrels of oil, a quantity about equal to all of Alaska's oil resources.

Reprocessing of spent fuel, however, is not currently being performed in this country, pending government decision on whether it will be allowed. Eventually, the spent fuel must either be transported to a reprocessing plant to recover its energy value or to a repository for long-term disposal.

How is spent fuel reprocessed?

Reprocessing is a chemical means of dissolving the solid spent fuel from a nuclear reactor and separating valuable unused uranium and plutonium from waste products.

The spent fuel from a commercial reactor is in the form of 12-foot-long bundles of metal tubes containing thousands of tiny solid pellets of uranium about the size of the end of the little finger. In reprocessing, the bundles are chopped into small segments and the fuel pellets dissolved in strong acid. The unused uranium and plutonium can then be chemically separated from waste materials, converted back into a solid and used as fuel again. The process can recover more than 99 percent of the usable fuel. The liquid chemicals containing the wastes will be converted into a solid for storage and ultimately permanent disposal.

What are nuclear wastes?

When a fuel bundle is placed in a commercial nuclear reactor, the fuel consists of pure uranium oxide—a material so low in radioactivity a person can handle the solid fuel pellets. After three to four years in a reactor's core, the 12-foot-long bundle of metal tubes holding the solid uranium pellets is removed from the reactor. At this point the bundle still looks virtually the same as when placed in the reactor. When the fuel bundle was fresh, it was 100 percent pure uranium oxide. After it is "spent," it is still about 96 percent pure uranium oxide. Of the difference, about 3 percent is the nuclear waste produced during the fissioning process which is virtually all locked within the solid fuel pellets.

In essence, nuclear waste is a collection of new elements resulting from the fission process and locked up in the fuel. When the large atoms of uranium are split ("fissioned" to release energy) materials are formed called fission products. These new, smaller atoms are different elements, including iodine, strontium, carbon, xenon, cesium, and even silver and palladium. Many of these new atoms are unstable and thus radioactive. These are the nuclear wastes.

In addition to the fission products, the nuclear process also results in some atoms being formed that are larger than the original uranium atoms, because some uranium atoms capture neutrons. These are called transuranics, of which the most well known is plutonium.

Most of the fission products are short lived and quite radioactive, with lifespans measured in tens of years or less. Some of the transuranics, on the other hand, have very low radioactivity but last much longer—some for thousands of years.

The fact that nuclear wastes are radioactive means they are decaying, i.e., the radioactivity is disappearing as heat. In the first six months after a spent fuel bundle is removed from a reactor's core, some 98 percent of the radioactivity decays and disappears. Forty to 50 years after being removed from the core, the radioactivity in the spent fuel decreases 100-fold.

There are, however, a number of classifications for nuclear wastes, determined primarily by the concentration of radioactive materials, the source and the form of the waste.

—High-Level Wastes: These are the fission-product wastes separated from the recovered fuel materials through reprocessing by chemically dissolving spent fuel. The high-level wastes from reprocessing are liquids which ultimately are chemically treated and converted to solids. Final disposal of these will be in deep underground stable geologic waste repositories, isolated from the environment.

—Transuranic Wastes: Presently, these come primarily from the defense program and will be produced also when reprocessing is performed. They are small quantities of liquid or solid waste that are contaminated with small amounts of plutonium and other transuranic elements.

—Low-Level Wastes: These include anything that is contaminated with low levels of radioactivity; for instance, clean-up liquids, rags, protective clothing, tools, machinery, and medical and research materials.

—Uranium mine and mill tailings: These are the residues, sludges, and sands from uranium mining and milling operations. They contain small concentrations of natural radioactive elements such as radium.

How much nuclear waste is there?

The commercial nuclear industry, to date, has accumulated about 9,000 tons of spent fuel, with some 1,500 tons being added annually. By 2000, a total of 100,000 tons of spent fuel will have been discharged from power reactors, so at that time there would be about 3,000 tons of actual waste. The military nuclear program has accumulated a volume of nuclear waste about 100 times greater than commercial power reactor waste, but the total amount of radioactivity in military waste is about the same as in the commercial waste since the military wastes are of lower radioactivity.

To put this amount of material into perspective, it is worth noting that industry in the United States produces each year a volume of toxic wastes some 10,000 times greater than the entire nuclear industry has produced since its beginning. Thus, by most commercial standards, the quantity of waste produced by the generation of electricity from nuclear power is small. If nuclear-generated electricity was used exclusively for life by one person, the amount of solid high-level waste would be half the volume of a soft-drink can.

As for the low-level wastes, some two million cubic feet are generated and disposed of each year in engineered, shallow land burial. Some 75 percent of all low-level waste is of military origin, and of the balance, about half comes from hospitals and educational and research activities. The balance comes from nuclear power plants.

The wastes generated by uranium mining and milling, some 10 to 15 million tons a year, are stored in piles at the mine sites. Again, this quantity is small in comparison with the mining wastes from extraction of other minerals. For example, mining copper in the U.S. results in the production of some 500 million tons of tailings a year, wastes that have characteristics very similar to those of uranium tailings in that they contain concentrations of toxic chemicals and low levels of radioactivity.

How is radioactive waste transported safely?

Several hazards are considered in the transportation of nuclear fuel and wastes, including radioactivity, ability to form a critical mass, theft, fire, and various types of accidents.

The first two hazards are controlled by the use of appropriate shielding and by separating materials. Others are preventable by a combination of impenetrable shipping materials and security personnel. All are subject to federal regulation.

Spent fuel assemblies have been, and will be, shipped in specially constructed casks to a storage facility or fuel reprocessing plant where reusable fuel materials would be separated from wastes. Similar casks will be used when shipping the high-level wastes. Controls and regulations which take into account both normal and accidental conditions already have been established by the NRC and the Department of Transportation.

Each shipping cask must withstand the following accident conditions, in sequence, without leaking:
  1. A 30-foot free drop onto a flat, unyielding horizontal surface (such as a concrete pad) with the cask oriented to cause maximum damage.

2. A 40-inch free drop onto the pointed end of a 6-inch diameter, 8-inch high steel bar, again with the cask oriented to cause maximum damage.
3. Exposure to a 1,475°F fire for 30 minutes with no artificial post-fire cooling.
4. Immersion in water to a depth of 3 feet for at least 8 hours immediately following the fire test.

A cask must be able to undergo these accident conditions in the order listed and remain in safe condition. No other hazardous shipping material container is designed to standards as stringent as these.

Each cask must be licensed by the NRC before use. Permission for use of the cask must be granted by the Department of Transportation. It must be demonstrated that the cask design meets all of the regulatory requirements before either agency gives approval. In addition, the license is contingent upon continued maintenance of the casks. The regulatory agencies have the power to check the casks any time after issuance of the license.

To put the transportation of nuclear waste and nuclear materials into perspective, consider that each year some 100 million shipments in the United States involve hazardous materials, such as flammables, explosives, poisons, etc. Two percent of those involve radioactive materials. To date, there have been more than one million shipments of radioactive materials, mostly for medical purposes, with a lower than average vehicle accident rate. No one has ever been injured due to radiation exposure from the 4,000 spent fuel assemblies transported to date in the United States.

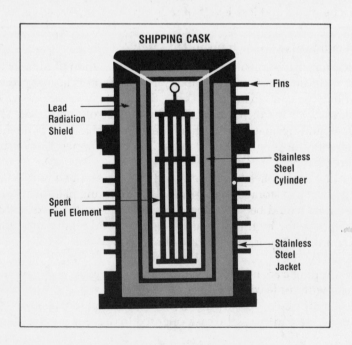

How should nuclear wastes be disposed of?

Great public and political concern has been created by the incorrect impression that scientists and engineers do not know how to dispose safely of high-level and other nuclear wastes. The simple fact is there are a number of safe and well-understood methods for disposing of nuclear wastes, but there is no urgency from a technical or health standpoint, and government has repeatedly postponed decisions on which of the several alternatives to permit.

High-level nuclear wastes can be converted into a solid form (if not already that way) and buried a half-mile or so underground in a stable geological environment.

There have been, quite literally, hundreds of studies on the feasibility and safety of nuclear waste disposal. All arrive at essentially the same conclusion: "Nuclear waste and radioactive effluents can be safely and reliably managed with existing technologies or a straightforward extension thereof." This recent consensus statement comes from The Coordinating Committee on Energy, a working committee of representatives from 22 major engineering societies having a combined membership of more than 700,000 engineers.

Confidence in the ability to isolate nuclear wastes safely from the environment comes from a four-barrier approach.

First, the radioactive wastes are immobilized by embedding them in stable, nondissolvable solid ceramic or glassy materials—actually making them a part of those materials, quite different from the impression some have that the wastes would be in glass bottles.

Second, the waste in this form is sealed in a ceramic or metal cannister.

Third, an absorbent mineral filling is packed around the cannister.

Finally, the entire assembly is sealed in deep bedrock of long geological stability and well isolated from the environment.

While there are uncertainties about a few of the specific details in any plan of this nature, the multiple barrier approach makes it unnecessary to have precise knowledge of geological factors, according to scientists. It is the overall performance of the system that is important.

What if mistakes are made in disposing of nuclear wastes?

In any design and process it is always possible for mistakes to occur. By providing a series of different, independent barriers in waste disposal, the possibility of mistakes or problems with all of the safeguards at once is greatly reduced. This is the essence of the approach to nuclear waste disposal. Nonetheless, the question "what if?" is still asked. Answers can be provided.

A Swedish proposal for disposing of spent fuel deep underground using the barrier concept has addressed the worst circumstances of the geologic barrier being penetrated by water. In this case, a person getting wellwater from the vicinity of the waste disposal site would get a maximum annual radiation exposure of only about 10 percent of the annual exposure from natural background sources.

In examining all the most recent data and proposals, the U.S. Department of Energy in its final environmental impact statement on the *Management of Commercially Generated Radioactive Waste* (October 1980) said: "In the worst case of general contamination of water, not more than one radiation-related fatality was projected to result over a 10,000 year period."

Will disposing of nuclear wastes be prohibitively expensive?

No. In its final environmental impact statement on the *Management of Commercially Generated Radioactive Waste*, the U.S. Department of Energy examined the total costs for waste disposal, including all waste treatment, storage, transportation, and the Department's own research and development for four different disposal mediums through 2040. The conclusion: "The cost of electricity in 1978 averaged 3.5¢ per kilowatt-hour over all types of services throughout the U.S. On that basis, the additional cost for waste management and disposal would add about 2 to 6 percent to the consumer's cost of electricity and no more than 3 percent if nuclear power growth to at least (250,000 MWe) is realized."

But don't nuclear wastes last almost forever, burdening future generations?

Radioactive wastes, by definition, decay with time. Many chemical wastes, on the other hand, do last forever. If nuclear wastes are safely and carefully stored in deep geological rock formations, it is highly improbable that they would ever present a problem for present or future generations.

The majority of the elements in nuclear waste decay very rapidly, so the radioactivity of spent fuel has decreased 100-fold in only 40 to 50 years. A small percentage of the nuclear wastes do last thousands of years. It is this small percentage that is often used to make the claim that it takes millions of years for *all* of the waste to disappear. While this is strictly true, it does not tell the whole story.

The danger posed by buried nuclear waste is that somehow, over very long periods of time, the waste cannister might be damaged and the glass or ceramic waste form might also be damaged, thereby allowing radioactive materials to enter underground water. Then, over hundreds and thousands of years again, this radioactively contaminated water might mix with the drinking water supply of a future generation.

In fact, however, after some 1,000 years, the toxicity of high-level wastes is about equal to the toxicity of the uranium ore from which the fuel originally was obtained. Interestingly, after about 4,000 years, the nuclear waste is no more toxic and therefore no more of a burden to future generations than natural mercury, chromium, cadmium, silver, or many other ores.

40

ANOTHER NUCLEAR FUEL—PLUTONIUM

Plutonium is an element. Chemically, it is similar to uranium and is radioactive. It is found rarely in nature, but can be produced by the fissioning of nuclear fuel. It remains in the fuel pellets until the spent fuel is reprocessed, so it is subject to continuing, detailed controls.

Since plutonium is a very chemically reactive element, it normally exists as an oxide which is insoluble in the human body. Consequently, the debate about the danger of plutonium hinges on whether minute particles of plutonium, if inhaled, would remain in the lungs and cause lung cancer.

About five tons of plutonium have been released to the biosphere from nuclear weapon detonations, but not one case of lung cancer ascribable to plutonium has been recorded. About 25 people inhaled large quantities of plutonium in laboratory accidents during nuclear weapons development in the 1940s. The substance remains in their bodies. One died recently of a heart attack. None has developed lung cancer.

But isn't plutonium "the most toxic substance known to man?"

Not by a long shot. The question itself requires examination.

"Toxicity" is a medical term defined as the inherent ability of a substance to produce injury once it reaches a particular tissue within the body. The uninformed allegation one sometimes hears or reads that "a single pound of plutonium could deliver millions of doses of lung cancer" is highly misleading, because plutonium is easily controlled and because only a very small fraction of any uncontrolled plutonium could conceivably get into human lungs.

Plutonium produced in the fissioning process in nuclear reactors can be unlocked from the rest of the spent fuel only by chemically reprocessing the fuel. Clearly this is a tightly controlled situation where quantities of the substance could not be released to the public. By contrast, consider the fact that the public is often exposed to other, uncontrolled poisons. People die each year from eating poisonous mushrooms, for example. Botulism is another killer. Children die each year from ingesting common household products.

The allegation that plutonium might kill millions is comparable to the statement that the amount of arsenic imported annually into the U.S. is sufficient to cause more than a billion human fatalities—a statement that, although true, ignores the fact that arsenic, however lethal, cannot and does not kill people who are not exposed to it. While arsenic tragically *is* responsible for deaths, by contrast, after more than two generations of nuclear power operations, neither scientists nor doctors know of a single case of death from inhaling plutonium.

What about safeguarding plutonium?

Plutonium can be used to fuel a nuclear reactor. Plutonium can also be used to make a nuclear bomb. For that reason, fears have been expressed about safeguarding the material. The NRC requires each licensee to have elaborate safeguarding programs and commercial nuclear plants to have their own security systems, which safeguard the plants and all of the fuel.

For more than 30 years, the military has safeguarded the use and shipment of plutonium produced specifically for the weapons program. None is known to have been stolen.

It should be noted that other nations possess plutonium and other nations possess nuclear bombs. Nonproliferation of nuclear weapons is an important issue, and the spread of nuclear weapons should be prevented. More efficient and less costly paths are available for a foreign nation to develop nuclear weapons than through a commercial nuclear power program. U.S. nuclear power plant operations do not contribute in any way to foreign nuclear weapons proliferation.

Can plutonium or enriched uranium be stolen from nuclear facilities?

It would be extremely difficult.

There are few places in the U.S. where plutonium or enriched uranium are concentrated; there are no commercial fabricators of plutonium fuels and only three fabricators of special fuels that use highly enriched uranium. The risk of theft could increase when a number of reprocessing plants may be operating and when plutonium may be used as a reactor fuel, but reliable safeguard procedures will be in effect before then.

From a practical point of view, theft of used reactor fuel containing plutonium would be difficult. For example, a crude bomb using twenty-five pounds of plutonium would require the theft of about 1,500 pounds of radioactive fuel, removed from 12-foot long reactor fuel elements transported in a shipping container weighing up to 100 tons. Direct exposure of a thief to the radioactive fuel, if one tried to remove the rods from the container, would be fatal.

Can the threat of dispersal of radioactive materials be an effective terrorist device?

Probably not.

For this purpose, terrorists would need to be in possession of substances so radioactive that it is extremely unlikely they would be able to handle or even survive the materials themselves.

Large quantities of highly radioactive materials are not easily obtainable. Materials less intensely radioactive, and thus easier to handle, have the distinct disadvantage (from the viewpoint of terrorism) of causing no effects on people, plants, or animals at least for decades after exposure. While it is clear that members of the public would be frightened by the prospect of exposure to excessive amounts of radiation, it is not clear how anyone would know they had been exposed. In contrast, it would be possible to affect far greater numbers of people with a variety of easily obtainable chemical and biological poisons.

How difficult would it be to build a nuclear bomb if one could obtain the basic materials?

It appears to be a widespread belief that so much has been published about nuclear bombs that almost anyone with a calculator, technical learning, and some plutonium could make a nuclear bomb. This myth was reinforced recently when the press carried stories about two students at the Massachusetts Institute of Technology and Princeton, who were alleged actually to have designed nuclear bombs with little more than information available in unclassified reports.

In his book, *Hans Bethe, Prophet of Energy*, Jeremy Bernstein asked Dr. Bethe, a Nobel laureate in physics and member of the Manhattan Project team during World War II: "Suppose one had available all the open literature on making a bomb, including these student papers; and one had all the enriched uranium or plutonium that one needed—where would one be in the construction of an atomic bomb?" Dr. Bethe's answer: "Nowhere."

The fact that the general principles of nuclear weapons are well understood is not sufficient to overcome a variety of complex technical problems never mentioned in popular articles.

How extensive a security program is necessary to protect nuclear materials? Will such a program curtail civil liberties?

The security personnel required for the present nuclear industry is a few thousand people, a small part of the total number of persons employed in industrial security. This will grow by a factor of two or three by 2000. Security checks that are, or could be, required for people with access to nuclear materials are common in industry. Security for the nuclear industry need not restrict our freedom or civil liberties any more than the use of armored cars and bank guards has resulted in a police state.

Does selling nuclear power plant components abroad, where we can't control their use, increase the danger of nuclear bomb proliferation?

Not really, because atomic bomb materials are obtainable from sources other than commercial power plants. However, controls are needed, so the U.S. and other nuclear nations have placed restrictions of various sorts on their nuclear sales abroad. These include embargoes of power plants to nations perceived as likely to be involved in armed conflicts. Another common restriction can be to keep fuel reprocessing in the country from which the fuel originated, and to keep secret the uranium enrichment process.

The International Atomic Energy Agency, treaties, sales agreements, security agencies, and other instruments all are working to deter the misuse of nuclear technology.

NUCLEAR POWER—LOOKING AHEAD

It appears we have a sufficient nuclear fuel supply for the time being. The current proven reserves of uranium in the United States are sufficient to supply all fuel needs for the lifetimes of all the reactors now built, under construction, or planned. However, if we are not to use up this resource the same way we are using up some fossil fuel resources, we need to make more efficient use of nuclear fuels.

The energy value of current proven reserves of uranium ore are about 50 percent greater than the energy value of proven U.S. oil reserves. Uranium, however, has an interesting advantage over fossil fuels. If the uranium fuel is used in a breeder reactor (see "What is a breeder reactor?") instead of in current conventional reactors, the effective value of U.S. uranium resources would be increased about 60 times, stretching some 40 years' worth of uranium into many centuries' worth of fuel.

Nuclear power, then, has an energy potential far greater than coal, oil, and gas combined. As more and more electric generating capacity is changed to nuclear, more and more fossil fuels will be freed for the other productive uses to which they are uniquely suited, such as making plastics, fertilizers, medicines, and liquid synthetic fuels. Coal will remain as another of the most preferable fuels to make electricity, but neither it nor nuclear can do the job alone. Thus, nuclear power in the future will supplement other sources of energy, not replace them.

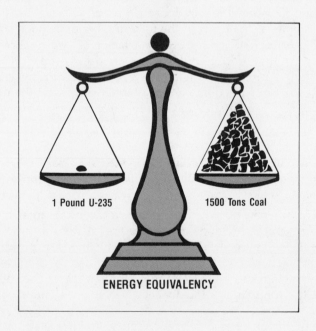

1 Pound U-235   1500 Tons Coal

ENERGY EQUIVALENCY

What is a breeder reactor?

A "breeder" is a reactor that produces more nuclear fuel than it uses. As nuclear fuel is consumed in the chain reaction process, by-products are formed that, when refined and separated from waste materials, can be used again for nuclear fuel.

Fissionable fuels, such as uranium-235 and plutonium-239, produce the heat energy required to operate a power plant. Certain nonfissionable or "fertile" materials, such as U-238, will convert or change into fissionable fuel such as Pu-239 by absorbing some of the neutrons freed during the fission process.

All reactors produce plutonium that can be refined into additional fuel. Those reactors that produce a smaller amount of fissionable fuel than they consume are called converters. Those that produce more fissionable fuel than they started with are called breeders.

It is important to remember that the reactor must be shut down periodically to provide fresh fuel and the spent fuel must be removed and reprocessed to separate the waste materials from the recoverable fissionable fuel to permit its subsequent use.

There are several kinds of breeder reactors currently in the development stage; the liquid metal-cooled fast breeder reactor (LMFBR) is the best known, most prominent and preferred. The U.S. initiated this technology, but has been slow in developing it as a commercial system. At this time, we are several years behind the USSR and Western European countries in LMFBR demonstration plants because of political controversy in the United States.

Other possible types of breeder reactors include the gas-cooled breeder reactor (GCBR) and the light water breeder reactor (LWBR), in which fertile thorium is converted into fissionable uranium-233. The LWBR may actually produce less fissionable fuel than it consumes and not be a true breeder, but rather an advanced converter.

While there is much uranium in the world, only about 0.7 percent of it is fissionable and useful as fuel for today's reactors. The remaining amount, 99.3 percent, is fertile uranium-238 which may be converted into fissionable material in breeder reactors. Thorium is a fertile element found in greater supplies than uranium throughout the U.S. and the world which could also be converted into fissionable material.

With conservation of natural energy resources a must in today's world, breeders can dramatically stretch available supplies of uranium and increase the efficiency of this resource. Because of the physical limit of economical uranium in the world, the current reactor systems will consume this resource within a few decades. However, the use of breeder reactors will permit the nuclear option to provide electricity for many, many centuries.

What happens to old reactors? What is decommissioning?

Nuclear plants are estimated to have an economically useful life of 30 to

40 years. At the end of that time, they may be worn out and new plants eventually may replace them. The new ones might use advanced light water reactors or a different nuclear technology, such as fusion or energy from some as yet undeveloped source.

Critics have sometimes charged there will be an insurmountable problem in dismantling—"decommissioning"—today's reactors. This is not so.

In the past, factories and conventional power stations simply have been destroyed, often with no special care or attention to prevent hazardous materials, when present, from being spread into the environment. This practice is in sharp contrast to that of the commercial nuclear industry.

At the end of its useful life, a nuclear plant will contain materials, structures and worn-out equipment, some of which are radioactive. Once the spent fuel and cooling water have been removed, most of the remaining radioactivity is located in and just around the reactor vessel. The major part of the plant never becomes radioactive and can be demolished or re-used without any restrictions.

The radioactive reactor parts will be treated as nuclear waste, and carefully disposed of with other forms of nuclear waste.

There is already a large amount of decommissioning experience around the world. Since 1960, the U.S. has decommissioned 68 small nuclear reactors.

Based on experience over the past 20 years and the fact that most of the decommissioning is simply a demolition operation, it is possible to provide a reasonable estimate for decommissioning costs. Various studies have arrived at decommissioning costs ranging from 4 to 10 percent of the original construction cost of the nuclear station. If it is assumed that decommissioning will cost 10 percent of original construction, this would add only about one-twentieth of one cent to each kilowatt-hour of electricity produced by any nuclear station.

What would be the consequences of stopping nuclear plant production?

Stopping the use of nuclear power would have serious short- and long-term effects. In the short term, those areas of the nation that depend heavily on nuclear electricity would suffer serious energy shortages and economic setbacks. In the longer term, the United States would find itself without one of the few significant and proven sources of new energy and would settle into the world's technical backwaters as other nations forged ahead.

The science and technology of nuclear energy exists. The nuclear genie cannot be stuffed back in the bottle and should not be if people are to have the energy they need. The prudent path for the U.S. to take is that of seeking the most economic, safe, and sensible means for using this technology. Furthermore, by providing technological leadership, the United States can play an influential role in nuclear safety in the international community.

It is clear that nuclear energy has an important role with respect to the United States electric energy industry. The recently completed National Academy of Sciences' study of the U.S. energy situation, *Energy in Transition 1985–2010*, pointed to the fact that coal and nuclear are the only major sources of energy available until the turn of the century. Study after study, both here and abroad, has reached the same conclusion.

While conservation extends available energy supplies, and in that regard is considered an energy source, it does not make more energy. The alternative sources now under intensive study, such as solar and wind, simply cannot meet the large needs of our society in so short a time.

In its 1980 year-end study, *Proposed Changes to Generating Capacity 1980–1989 for the Contiguous United States*, the Department of Energy (DOE) pointed out that some 35 percent of the new capacity to be added through 1989 is nuclear. DOE also estimated that if all of the nuclear and coal-fired capacity planned for 1985 is brought on line, the use of oil for electricity production would decrease to 20 percent of the amount used in 1980. If no new nuclear units are brought on line, the oil needed to produce electricity could actually increase by about 20 percent.

NERC also points to the need for bringing on line all of the currently planned coal and nuclear generating stations. It estimates that the oil needed to generate electricity could double by 1989, rather than decrease, if current trends continue and new coal and nuclear plants suffer additional delays.

A complete abandonment of commercial nuclear energy would not significantly affect military use of the technology, which is the real concern of some critics, nor would it affect the desire of other nations to use the technology to free themselves from dependence on imported oil. It would, however, have the following results.

- To shut down the 56,000 megawatts of nuclear capacity now operative would increase oil imports by approximately 1.75 million barrels a day and would cost electric consumers approximately $2 to $10 billion a year in increased fuel charges alone. Further, consumers would have to pay the capital charges associated with building alternative coal generating units at a cost of approximately $75 billion, as well as the huge write-offs involved in scrapping nuclear capacity.

- To abandon the construction work in progress on 90,500 megawatts of new, planned nuclear capacity would increase oil imports by 3.33 million barrels a day, if the capacity were to be replaced with oil-fired generators. At today's oil prices, that could cost electric consumers an estimated $19 billion a year in additional fuel charges. Further, consumers would have to pay the capital charges necessary to amortize the $50 billion already expended toward completion of these units.

- To forswear nuclear generation would place very heavy pressure on our nation's coal resources and aggravate environmental problems associated with fossil-fuel burning, including the potential problem of increasing carbon dioxide in the earth's atmosphere. It is very doubtful that coal mines could be developed and transportation facilities built rapidly enough in this century to fill the gap left by total cessation of nuclear generation. The U.S. General Accounting Office has predicted coal could not fill this gap unless the growth in electric consumption were kept below 2 percent a year, foreshadowing dire consequences for the entire economy should nuclear generation be abandoned.

What is new in nuclear technology?

Technology of any kind is always in transition. It is always changing. What seemed the ultimate machine or technique yesterday is often outmoded by tomorrow. Today's generation of nuclear power plants are even now being improved.

Scores of new reactor ideas and proposals are being discussed, in sizes ranging from small enough to heat a building to large enough to heat a city as well as produce electricity.

One of the most exciting of potential future nuclear technologies is called fusion. It is the opposite of fission. Fusion has the potential of providing even larger releases of working energy from an equal amount of fuel.

However, starting and sustaining the fusion process requires temperatures greater than those of the sun. The sun is a large nuclear fusion reactor operating on a continuous basis, and the solar energy we receive is a byproduct of nuclear fusion.

Despite 20 years of research and cooperative programs by most of the advanced countries of the world, no one has yet been able to sustain a fusion reaction in the laboratory. But researchers believe they are getting close. With the possibility of controlled fusion sometime after the turn of the century, electric utilities may be operating fusion-powered generating stations using fuel separated from ordinary seawater—an inexhaustible source.

Fusion technology is an important energy concept for the future.

COMMON ABBREVIATIONS

ACRS	Advisory Committee on Reactor Safeguards
AEC	Atomic Energy Commission (now the NRC and DOE)
ANS	American Nuclear Society
ASLB	Atomic Safety and Licensing Board
ASME	American Society of Mechanical Engineers
BWR	Boiling Water Reactor
CFR	Code of Federal Regulations
CP	Construction Permit
DOE	Department of Energy
ECCS	emergency core cooling system
EPA	Environmental Protection Agency
HTGR	High-Temperature Gas-cooled Reactor
KV	kilovolt
KW	kilowatt
KWH	kilowatt-hour
LMFBR	Liquid Metal Fast Breeder Reactor
LOCA	loss-of-coolant accident
LWR	Light Water Reactor
MWe	megawatts electrical
MWt	megawatts thermal
NRC	Nuclear Regulatory Commission
OL	Operating License
PSAR	Preliminary Safety Analysis Report
Pu	plutonium
PWR	Pressurized Water Reactor
U-235	uranium 235
UO_2	uranium dioxide

NUCLEAR POWER STATISTICS

Foreign Nations

179 Reactors Operating	....	79,735 MWe
160 Reactors under construction	....	133,605 MWe
27 Reactors on order	....	21,285 MWe
242 Reactors planned	....	234,904 MWe
608 Total	....	469,529 MWe

United States

77 Reactors with Operating Licenses[1]	....	58,353 MWe[2]
73 Reactors with Construction Permits	....	81,094 MWe
9 Reactors On Order	....	10,086 MWe
159 Total	....	149,533 MWe

[1]Includes the following units:

- Humboldt Bay, 65 MWe, shut down 7/2/76 pending a decision on whether to make seismic and other modifications or to decomission.
- Three Mile Island 1, 819 MWe, shut down in accordance with a Nuclear Regulatory Commission (NRC) restraining order pending completion of modifications and other actions related to the accident at Three Mile Island 2.
- Three Mile Island 2, 906 MWe, shut down since the accident on 3/28/79.
- Dresden 1, 200 MWe, shut down 10/31/78 for upgrading of its emergency core cooling system and for chemical cleaning. Outage expected to last through mid-1986, according to the NRC.
- Shippingport, 60 MWe, and N Reactor, 850 MWe; authorized for operation by the Department of Energy.

[2]Represents rated capability.

NUCLEAR POWER PLANTS IN THE U.S.
(April 1, 1982)

This list includes only commercial generating units on order, with construction permit, or operating license. Utilities having a 20 percent or greater interest in any particular unit are listed in parentheses after the operating utility. Brackets indicate participants in cooperative nuclear projects. Status is indicated by: O—order; C—construction permit.

The reactor types listed are: Pressurized Water Reactor—PWR; Boiling Water Reactor—BWR; High Temperature Gas-cooled Reactor—HTGR; Liquid Metal Fast Breeder Reactor—LMFBR; Light Water Breeder Reactor—LWBR. The reactor manufacturers are: Allis-Chalmers—AC; Babcock & Wilcox—B&W; Combustion Engineering—CE; General Atomic—GA; General Electric—GE; and Westinghouse—W. A single asterisk indicates that the plant has been deferred indefinitely and the new start-up date has not been announced.

State and Utility	Plant	Location	Net MWe	Type/Mfr.	Comm'l Operation
ALABAMA					
Alabama Power Co.	Joseph M. Farley 1	Houston County	829	PWR/W	1977
Alabama Power Co.	Joseph M. Farley 2	Houston County	829	PWR/W	1981
Tennessee Valley Authority	Browns Ferry 1	Decatur	1,065	BWR/GE	1974
Tennessee Valley Authority	Browns Ferry 2	Decatur	1,065	BWR/GE	1975
Tennessee Valley Authority	Browns Ferry 3	Decatur	1,065	BWR/GE	1977
Tennessee Valley Authority	Bellefonte 1 (C)	Scottsboro	1,235	PWR/B&W	1987
Tennessee Valley Authority	Bellefonte 2 (C)	Scottsboro	1,235	PWR/B&W	1988
ARIZONA					
Arizona Public Service Co. (Salt River Project)	Palo Verde 1 (C)	Wintersburg	1,270	PWR/CE	1983
Arizona Public Service Co. (Salt River Project)	Palo Verde 2 (C)	Wintersburg	1,270	PWR/CE	1984
Arizona Public Service Co. (Salt River Project)	Palo Verde 3 (C)	Wintersburg	1,270	PWR/CE	1986

State and Utility	Plant	Location	Net MWe	Type/Mfr.	Comm'l Operation
ARKANSAS					
Arkansas Power & Light Co.	Arkansas Nuclear One—1	Russellville	850	PWR/B&W	1974
Arkansas Power & Light Co.	Arkansas Nuclear One—2	Russellville	912	PWR/CE	1979
CALIFORNIA					
Pacific Gas and Electric Co.	Humboldt Bay	Humboldt Bay	65	BWR/GE	1963**
Pacific Gas and Electric Co.	Diablo Canyon 1 (C)	Avila Beach	1,084	PWR/W	1982
Pacific Gas and Electric Co.	Diablo Canyon 2 (C)	Avila Beach	1,106	PWR/W	1982
Sacramento Municipal Utility District	Rancho Seco 1	Clay Station	918	PWR/B&W	1975
Southern California Edison Co.	San Onofre 1	San Clemente	436	PWR/W	1968
(San Diego Gas and Electric Co.)					
Southern California Edison Co.	San Onofre 2 (C)	San Clemente	1,100	PWR/CE	1982
(San Diego Gas and Electric Co.)					
Southern California Edison Co.	San Onofre 3 (C)	San Clemente	1,100	PWR/CE	1983
(San Diego Gas and Electric Co.)					
COLORADO					
Public Service Company of Colorado	Fort St. Vrain	Platteville	330	HTGR/GA	1979
CONNECTICUT					
Connecticut Yankee Atomic Power Co.	Connecticut Yankee	Haddam Neck	575	PWR/W	1968
Northeast Nuclear Energy Co.	Millstone 1	Waterford	660	BWR/GE	1970
Northeast Nuclear Energy Co.	Millstone 2	Waterford	830	PWR/CE	1975
Northeast Nuclear Energy Co.	Millstone 3 (C)	Waterford	1,150	PWR/W	1986
FLORIDA					
Florida Power Corp.	Crystal River 3	Red Level	825	PWR/B&W	1977
Florida Power & Light Co.	Turkey Point 3	Turkey Point	693	PWR/W	1972
Florida Power & Light Co.	Turkey Point 4	Turkey Point	693	PWR/W	1973
Florida Power & Light Co.	St. Lucie 1	St. Lucie County	802	PWR/CE	1976
Florida Power & Light Co.	St. Lucie 2 (C)	St. Lucie County	842	PWR/CE	1983

52

GEORGIA

Georgia Power Co. (Oglethorpe Electric Membership Corp.)	Edwin I. Hatch 1	Baxley	786	BWR/GE	1975
Georgia Power Co. (Oglethorpe Electric Membership Corp.)	Edwin I. Hatch 2	Baxley	790	BWR/GE	1979
Georgia Power Co. (Oglethorpe Electric Membership Corp.)	Alvin W. Vogtle 1 (C)	Waynesboro	1,100	PWR/W	1987
Georgia Power Co. (Oglethorpe Electric Membership Corp.)	Alvin W. Vogtle 2 (C)	Waynesboro	1,100	PWR/W	1988

ILLINOIS

Commonwealth Edison Co.	Dresden 1	Morris	207	BWR/GE	1960
Commonwealth Edison Co.	Dresden 2	Morris	794	BWR/GE	1970
Commonwealth Edison Co.	Dresden 3	Morris	794	BWR/GE	1971
Commonwealth Edison Co.	Zion 1	Zion	1,040	PWR/W	1973
Commonwealth Edison Co.	Zion 2	Zion	1,040	PWR/W	1973
Commonwealth Edison Co. (Iowa-Illinois Gas and Electric Co.)	Quad Cities 1	Cordova	789	BWR/GE	1972
Commonwealth Edison Co. (Iowa-Illinois Gas and Electric Co.)	Quad Cities 2	Cordova	789	BWR/GE	1972
Commonwealth Edison Co.	LaSalle 1 (C)	Seneca	1,078	BWR/GE	1982
Commonwealth Edison Co.	LaSalle 2 (C)	Seneca	1,078	BWR/GE	1983
Commonwealth Edison Co.	Braidwood 1 (C)	Braidwood	1,120	PWR/W	1985
Commonwealth Edison Co.	Braidwood 2 (C)	Braidwood	1,120	PWR/W	1986
Commonwealth Edison Co.	Byron 1 (C)	Byron	1,120	PWR/W	1984
Commonwealth Edison Co.	Byron 2 (C)	Byron	1,120	PWR/W	1985
Commonwealth Edison Co. (Iowa-Illinois Gas and Electric Co., Interstate Power Co.)	Carroll County 1 (O)	Savanna	1,100	PWR/W	1999
Commonwealth Edison Co. (Iowa-Illinois Gas and Electric Co., Interstate Power Co.)	Carroll County 2 (O)	Savanna	1,120	PWR/W	2000
Illinois Power Co.	Clinton 1 (C)	Clinton	950	BWR/GE	1983
Illinois Power Co.	Clinton 2 (C)	Clinton	950	BWR/GE	Indef.*

State and Utility	Plant	Location	Net MWe	Type/Mfr.	Comm'l Operation
INDIANA					
Northern Indiana Public Service Co.	Bailly Nuclear 1 (C)	Dunes Acres	644	BWR/GE	1989
Public Service Indiana	Marble Hill 1 (C)	Madison	1,130	PWR/W	1986
Public Service Indiana	Marble Hill 2 (C)	Madison	1,130	PWR/W	1987
IOWA					
Iowa Electric Light and Power Co. (Central Iowa Power Cooperative)	Duane Arnold	Palo	538	BWR/GE	1974
Iowa Power and Light Co. (Central Iowa Power Cooperative, Associated Electric Cooperative of Missouri)	Vandalia (O)	Vandalia	1,270	PWR/B&W	Indef.*
KANSAS					
Kansas Gas and Electric Co. (Kansas City Power & Light Co.)	Wolf Creek (C)	Burlington	1,150	PWR/W	1984
LOUISIANA					
Gulf States Utilities Co.	River Bend 1 (C)	St. Francisville	934	BWR/GE	1984
Gulf States Utilities Co.	River Bend 2 (C)	St. Francisville	934	BWR/GE	Indef.*
Louisiana Power & Light Co.	Waterford 3 (C)	Taft	1,165	PWR/CE	1983
MAINE					
Maine Yankee Atomic Power Co.	Maine Yankee	Wiscasset	825	PWR/CE	1972
MARYLAND					
Baltimore Gas and Electric Co.	Calvert Cliffs 1	Lusby	845	PWR/CE	1975
Baltimore Gas and Electric Co.	Calvert Cliffs 2	Lusby	845	PWR/CE	1977
MASSACHUSETTS					
Boston Edison Co.	Pilgrim 1	Plymouth	655	BWR/GE	1972

MASSACHUSETTS *(continued)*

Company	Plant	Location	MW	Type	Date
Boston Edison Co.	Pilgrim 2 (O)	Plymouth	1,150	PWR/CE	Indef.*
Yankee Atomic Electric Co.	Yankee	Rowe	175	PWR/W	1961

MICHIGAN

Company	Plant	Location	MW	Type	Date
Consumers Power Co.	Big Rock Point	Big Rock Point	63	BWR/GE	1962
Consumers Power Co.	Palisades	South Haven	740	PWR/CE	1971
Consumers Power Co.	Midland 1 (C)	Midland	524	PWR/B&W	1984
Consumers Power Co.	Midland 2 (C)	Midland	806	PWR/B&W	1983
Detroit Edison Co.	Enrico Fermi 2 (C)	Lagoona Beach	1,093	BWR/GE	1983
Indiana & Michigan Electric Co.	Donald C. Cook 1	Bridgman	1,054	PWR/W	1975
Indiana & Michigan Electric Co.	Donald C. Cook 2	Bridgman	1,100	PWR/W	1978

MINNESOTA

Company	Plant	Location	MW	Type	Date
Northern States Power Co.	Monticello	Monticello	545	BWR/GE	1971
Northern States Power Co.	Prairie Island 1	Red Wing	530	PWR/W	1973
Northern States Power Co.	Prairie Island 2	Red Wing	530	PWR/W	1974

MISSISSIPPI

Company	Plant	Location	MW	Type	Date
Mississippi Power & Light Co.	Grand Gulf 1 (C)	Port Gibson	1,250	BWR/GE	1982
Mississippi Power & Light Co.	Grand Gulf 2 (C)	Port Gibson	1,250	BWR/GE	Indef.*
Tennessee Valley Authority	Yellow Creek 1 (C)	Tishimingo County	1,285	PWR/CE	1990
Tennessee Valley Authority	Yellow Creek 2 (C)	Tishimingo County	1,285	PWR/CE	Indef.*

MISSOURI

Company	Plant	Location	MW	Type	Date
Union Electric Co.	Callaway 1 (C)	Callaway County	1,150	PWR/W	1984
Union Electric Co.	Callaway 2 (C)	Callaway County	1,150	PWR/W	1988

NEBRASKA

Company	Plant	Location	MW	Type	Date
Nebraska Public Power District	Cooper	Brownville	778	BWR/GE	1974
Omaha Public Power District	Fort Calhoun 1	Fort Calhoun	457	PWR/CE	1973

NEW HAMPSHIRE

Company	Plant	Location	MW	Type	Date
Public Service Co. of New Hampshire (United Illuminating Co.)	Seabrook 1 (C)	Seabrook	1,194	PWR/W	1984
Public Service Co. of New Hampshire (United Illuminating Co.)	Seabrook 2 (C)	Seabrook	1,194	PWR/W	1986

State and Utility	Plant	Location	Net MWe	Type/Mfr.	Comm'l Operation
NEW JERSEY					
Jersey Central Power & Light Co.	Oyster Creek	Toms River	650	BWR/GE	1969
Public Service Electric and Gas Co. (Philadelphia Electric Co.)	Salem 1	Lower Alloway Creek Township	1,090	PWR/W	1976
Public Service Electric and Gas Co. (Philadelphia Electric Co.)	Salem 2 (C)	Lower Alloway Creek Township	1,115	PWR/W	1981
Public Service Electric and Gas Co.	Hope Creek 1 (C)	Lower Alloway Creek Township	1,067	BWR/GE	1986
NEW YORK					
Consolidated Edison Co. of N.Y., Inc.	Indian Point 2	Buchanan	873	PWR/W	1974
Power Authority of the State of New York	Indian Point 3	Buchanan	965	PWR/W	1976
Power Authority of the State of New York	James A. FitzPatrick	Scriba	821	BWR/GE	1975
Long Island Lighting Co.	Shoreham (C)	Brookhaven	854	BWR/GE	1983
Niagara Mohawk Power Corp.	Nine Mile Point 1	Oswego	620	BWR/GE	1969
Niagara Mohawk Power Corp.	Nine Mile Point 2 (C)	Oswego	1,080	BWR/GE	1986
Rochester Gas and Electric Corp.	Robert E. Ginna	Rochester	470	PWR/W	1970
NORTH CAROLINA					
Carolina Power & Light Co.	Brunswick 1	Southport	821	BWR/GE	1977
Carolina Power & Light Co.	Brunswick 2	Southport	821	BWR/GE	1975
Carolina Power & Light Co.	Shearon Harris 1 (C)	New Hill	900	PWR/W	1985
Carolina Power & Light Co.	Shearon Harris 2 (C)	New Hill	900	PWR/W	1989
Duke Power Co.	William McGuire 1	Cowans Ford Dam	1,180	PWR/W	1981
Duke Power Co.	William McGuire 2 (C)	Cowans Ford Dam	1,180	PWR/W	1983
OHIO					
Cincinnati Gas & Electric Co. (Columbus and Southern Ohio Electric Co., Dayton Power and Light Co.)	Wm. H. Zimmer 1 (C)	Moscow	810	BWR/GE	1983

Owner	Plant	Location	Capacity	Type	Year
Central Area Power Coordination Group (CAPCO) [Cleveland Electric Illuminating Co. (operating utility), Duquesne Light Co., Ohio Edison, Co., Pennsylvania Power Co., Toledo Edison Co.]	Perry 1 (C)	North Perry	1,205	BWR/GE	1984
Central Area Power Coordination Group (CAPCO) [Cleveland Electric Illuminating Co. (operating utility), Duquesne Light Co., Ohio Edison Co., Pennsylvania Power Co., Toledo Edison Co.]	Perry 2 (C)	North Perry	1,205	BWR/GE	1988
Central Area Power Coordination Group (CAPCO) [Toledo Edison Co. (operating utility), Cleveland Electric Illuminating Co.]	Davis-Besse 1	Oak Harbor	906	PWR/B&W	1977

OREGON

Owner	Plant	Location	Capacity	Type	Year
Portland General Electric Co. (Eugene Water & Electric Board)	Trojan	Rainier	1,130	PWR/W	1976
Portland General Electric Co. (Pacific Power & Light Co., Puget Sound Power & Light Co., Pacific Northwest Generating Co.)	Pebble Springs 1 (O)	Arlington	1,260	PWR/B&W	Indef.*
Portland General Electric Co. (Pacific Power & Light Co., Puget Sound Power & Light Co.)	Pebble Springs 2 (O)	Arlington	1,260	PWR/B&W	Indef.*

PENNSYLVANIA

Owner	Plant	Location	Capacity	Type	Year
Duquesne Light Co.	Shippingport	Shippingport	60	PWR/W	1957
Central Area Power Coordination Group (CAPCO) [Duquesne Light Co. (operating utility), Ohio Edison Co., Pennsylvania Power Co.]	Beaver Valley 1	Shippingport	852	PWR/W	1977
Central Area Power Coordination Group (CAPCO) [Duquesne Light Co. (operating utility), Cleveland Electric Illuminating Co., Ohio Edison Co., Toledo Edison Co.]	Beaver Valley 2 (C)	Shippingport	852	PWR/W	1986

State and Utility	Plant	Location	Net MWe	Type/Mfr.	Comm'l Operation
PENNSYLVANIA *(continued)*					
Metropolitan Edison Co. (Jersey Central Power & Light Co., Pennsylvania Electric Co.)	Three Mile Island 1	Londonderry Township	800	PWR/B&W	1974
Metropolitan Edison Co. (Jersey Central Power & Light Co., Pennsylvania Electric Co.)	Three Mile Island 2	Londonderry Township	906	PWR/B&W	1978**
Pennsylvania Power & Light Co.	Susquehanna 1 (C)	Berwick	1,050	BWR/GE	1983
Pennsylvania Power & Light Co.	Susquehanna 2 (C)	Berwick	1,050	BWR/GE	1984
Philadelphia Electric Co. (Public Service Electric and Gas Co.)	Peach Bottom 2	Peach Bottom Township	1,065	BWR/GE	1974
Philadelphia Electric Co. (Public Service Electric and Gas Co.)	Peach Bottom 3	Peach Bottom Township	1,065	BWR/GE	1974
Philadelphia Electric Co.	Limerick 1 (C)	Limerick Township	1,065	BWR/GE	Indef.*
Philadelphia Electric Co.	Limerick 2 (C)	Limerick Township	1,065	BWR/GE	Indef.*
SOUTH CAROLINA					
Carolina Power & Light Co.	H.B. Robinson 2	Hartsville	700	PWR/W	1971
Duke Power Co.	Oconee 1	Lake Keowee	887	PWR/B&W	1973
Duke Power Co.	Oconee 2	Lake Keowee	887	PWR/B&W	1974
Duke Power Co.	Oconee 3	Lake Keowee	887	PWR/B&W	1974
Duke Power Co.	Catawba 1 (C)	York County	1,145	PWR/W	1984
Duke Power Co.	Catawba 2 (C)	York County	1,145	PWR/W	1985
Duke Power Co.	Cherokee 1 (C)	Cherokee County	1,280	PWR/CE	Indef.*
Duke Power Co.	Cherokee 2 (C)	Cherokee County	1,280	PWR/CE	Indef.*
Duke Power Co.	Cherokee 3 (C)	Cherokee County	1,280	PWR/CE	Indef.*
South Carolina Electric & Gas Co. (South Carolina Public Service Authority)	Virgil C. Summer 1 (C)	Parr	900	PWR/W	1982
TENNESSEE					
Tennessee Valley Authority	Sequoyah 1	Daisy	1,140	PWR/W	1981

Tennessee Valley Authority	Sequoyah 2	Daisy	1,140	PWR/W	1982
Tennessee Valley Authority	Watts Bar 1 (C)	Spring City	1,165	PWR/W	1984
Tennessee Valley Authority	Watts Bar 2 (C)	Spring City	1,165	PWR/W	1985
Tennessee Valley Authority	Hartsville A-1 (C)	Hartsville	1,205	BWR/GE	1991
Tennessee Valley Authority	Hartsville A-2 (C)	Hartsville	1,205	BWR/GE	1992
Tennessee Valley Authority	Hartsville B-1 (C)	Hartsville	1,205	BWR/GE	Indef.*
Tennessee Valley Authority	Hartsville B-2 (C)	Hartsville	1,205	BWR/GE	Indef.*
Tennessee Valley Authority	Phipps Bend 1 (C)	Surgoinsville	1,220	BWR/GE	Indef.*
Tennessee Valley Authority	Phipps Bend 2 (C)	Surgoinsville	1,220	BWR/GE	Indef.*
(Commonwealth Edison Co., U.S. Department of Energy)	Clinch River Breeder Reactor Plant (O)	Oak Ridge	350	LMFBR/W	Indef.*

TEXAS

Houston Lighting & Power Co.	Allens Creek 1 (O)	Wallis	1,150	BWR/GE	1991
South Texas Project [Houston Lighting & Power Co. (project manager), Central Power and Light Co., City Public Service Board of San Antonio, City of Austin]	South Texas Project 1 (C)	Matagorda County	1,250	PWR/W	1984
South Texas Project [Houston Lighting & Power Co. (project manager), Central Power and Light Co., City Public Service Board of San Antonio, City of Austin]	South Texas Project 2 (C)	Matagorda County	1,250	PWR/W	1986
Texas Utilities Generating Co. (Dallas Power & Light Co., Texas Electric Service Co., Texas Power & Light Co.)	Comanche Peak 1 (C)	Somervell County	1,150	PWR/W	1984
Texas Utilities Generating Co. (Dallas Power & Light Co., Texas Electric Service Co., Texas Power & Light Co.)	Comanche Peak 2 (C)	Somervell County	1,150	PWR/W	1985

VERMONT

| Vermont Yankee Nuclear Power Corp. | Vermont Yankee | Vernon | 514 | BWR/GE | 1972 |

State and Utility	Plant	Location	Net MWe	Type/Mfr.	Comm'l Operation
VIRGINIA					
Virginia Electric and Power Co.	Surry 1	Gravel Neck	822	PWR/W	1972
Virginia Electric and Power Co.	Surry 2	Gravel Neck	822	PWR/W	1973
Virginia Electric and Power Co.	North Anna 1	Mineral	907	PWR/W	1978
Virginia Electric and Power Co.	North Anna 2	Mineral	907	PWR/W	1980
Virginia Electric and Power Co.	North Anna 3 (C)	Mineral	907	PWR/B&W	1989
WASHINGTON					
Puget Sound Power and Light Co. (Portland General Electric Co., Pacific Power & Light Co.)	Skagit 1 (O)	Sedro Woolley	1,288	BWR/GE	Indef.*
Puget Sound Power and Light Co. (Portland General Electric Co., Pacific Power & Light Co.)	Skagit 2 (O)	Sedro Woolley	1,288	BWR/GE	Indef.*
Department of Energy (Power distributed by Washington Public Power Supply System)	Hanford—N	Richland	800	Graphite	1966
Washington Public Power Supply System	WPPSS 1 (C)	Richland	1,267	PWR/B&W	1986
Washington Public Power Supply System	WPPSS 2 (C)	Richland	1,103	BWR/GE	1984
Washington Public Power Supply System	WPPSS 3 (C)	Satsop	1,242	PWR/CE	1986
WISCONSIN					
Dairyland Power Cooperative	LaCrosse	Genoa	50	BWR/AC	1969
Wisconsin Electric Power Co.	Point Beach 1	Two Creeks	497	PWR/W	1970
Wisconsin Electric Power Co.	Point Beach 2	Two Creeks	497	PWR/W	1972
Wisconsin Public Service Corp. (Wisconsin Power and Light Co.)	Kewaunee	Carlton Township	535	PWR/W	1974

*Indefinitely delayed.
**Shut down. No decision on future operation.

SOURCES

Numerous scientific and informational sources were utilized in producing this chapter. In addition to Edison Electric Institute, the sources include the Department of Energy and other federal agencies; the American Nuclear Society; Duquesne Light Company; Consolidated Edison Company of New York, Inc.; and Texas Electric Service Company.

WHERE TO CALL

Additional information on nuclear power and answers to questions are available from the following government agencies and private organizations:

American Nuclear Society
La Grange Park, IL 312/352-6611
Arlington, VA 703/521-8806

Atomic Industrial Forum
Washington, D.C. 301/654-9260
New York, NY 212/599-1881

Edison Electric Institute
Washington, DC 202/828-7400

Electric Power Research Institute
Palo Alto, CA 415/855-2000
Washington, DC 202/872-9222

Institute of Nuclear Power Operations
Atlanta, GA 404/953-3600

Scientists and Engineers for Secure Energy, Inc.
1225 19th St., NW, Suite 415
Washington, D.C. 20036

U.S. Department of Energy
Office of Public Affairs
Washington, DC 202/252-5575

U.S. Nuclear Regulatory Commission
Office of Public Affairs
Bethesda, MD 301/492-7715

COAL

ANSWERS TO YOUR QUESTIONS

COAL: AN INTRODUCTION

Coal is our most plentiful fossil energy resource. Estimated recoverable reserves in the United States alone are capable of meeting our country's energy needs for at least the next 300 years, at today's consumption rates.

Coal was once a major source of energy, but its use declined with the increasing popularity of gas and oil. During the 1970s, however, coal consumption increased, the result of a number of factors such as the influence of OPEC. The electric utility industry remains the major coal consumer today, accounting for over 80 percent of the coal used in this country. In 1980, over half of the electric energy in this country was produced from coal.

With the increasing cost and limited availability of oil, coal is experiencing a new popularity. Industries are beginning to rediscover coal; utilities are converting oil-fired powerplants, when practical, to coal; and new technologies are being developed to permit cleaner burning of the fuel. A coal-burning ship has been ordered by one utility, and there is even talk of a new generation of coal-burning locomotives.

The purpose of this chapter is to acquaint you with coal: what it is, where it comes from, how it is used to produce electricity, and its future as an energy source.

COAL—WHAT IS IT?

Some 250 million years ago, much of America was a large swamp covered with dense forests and thick plant growth. As plants and trees died, they sank under the wet surface of the earth where there was not enough oxygen for them to decay. As new plant life grew to replace the dead plants and, in turn, died and sank into the swampy ground, many layers of dead plants accumulated. With geological changes over centuries, the plants were tightly compacted, then compressed. The result of this phenomenon is coal. Since coal is composed of once-living material, it is known as a "fossil fuel." Oil and natural gas are also fossil fuels.

What are the different kinds of coal?

Over millions of years the dead plants from prehistoric swamps were transformed into several different forms of coal:

- *Peat*—After layers of dead plants had been buried for thousands of years, they first were transformed into peat, a brownish-black substance that looks very much like decayed wood. It usually is found in swamps and bogs. When dried, peat will burn and produce heat.

- *Lignite*—As time passed, some layers of peat were pressed down into thinner layers of material called lignite. When burned, this brownish-black material produces more heat than peat, but it still has less heating value than bituminous coal. It is now used primarily in Texas and North Dakota for generating electricity.

- *Bituminous coal*—The continued pressure from the weight of earth and ocean changed much of the lignite in America into bituminous coal. Although this type of coal is harder than lignite, it is called "soft coal" because it can be broken easily into the right sizes for many uses. Coal that is not quite as hard as bituminous is called subbituminous. Bituminous and subbituminous coals are the most abundant coals in the United States, accounting for about 90 percent of demonstrated coal reserves.

- *Anthracite*—In a few places the pressure was so great that it changed the bituminous coal into anthracite, or "hard coal." Anthracite has a shiny black color. Compared with the other kinds of coal, there is not much anthracite in the United States. It is found primarily in northeastern Pennsylvania.

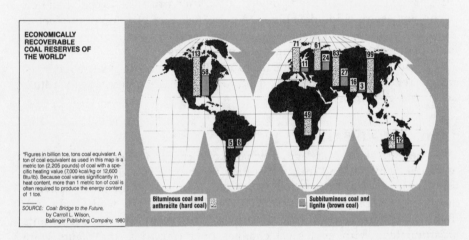

ECONOMICALLY RECOVERABLE COAL RESERVES OF THE WORLD*

*Figures in billion tce, tons coal equivalent. A ton of coal equivalent as used in this map is a metric ton (2,205 pounds) of coal with a specific heating value (7,000 kcal/kg or 12,600 Btu/lb). Because coal varies significantly in heat content, more than 1 metric ton of coal is often required to produce the energy content of 1 tce.

SOURCE: *Coal: Bridge to the Future*, by Carroll L. Wilson, Ballinger Publishing Company, 1980

Bituminous coal and anthracite (hard coal)

Subbituminous coal and lignite (brown coal)

How much coal is there?

The nation's identified coal resources, according to the U.S. Geological Survey, are approximately 1.7 trillion net tons, including beds down to three thousand feet below the surface, with an estimated 1.8 trillion net tons in unmapped and unexplored areas throughout the United states.

U.S. underground mines average less than 300 feet in depth and contain relatively level and thick coal seams, with most of the coal mined from beds two-and-one-half to eight feet thick. In some western areas, coal seams are as thick as 100 feet and are accessible by surface mining.

Not all the coal is recoverable, however. There is a difference between the total amount of coal deposited by nature (which geologists call *resources*) and the portion that can be developed for use (which they call *reserves*). The U.S. Geological Survey maintains information on all designated coal resources, and the U.S. Energy Information Administration is responsible for compiling estimates of the currently mineable coal reserve base in measured and indicated deposits.

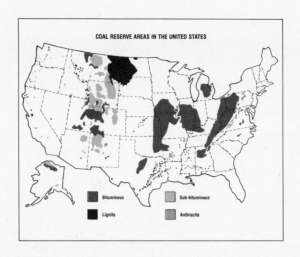

COAL RESERVE AREAS IN THE UNITED STATES

Bituminous Sub-bituminous

Lignite Anthracite

Where is coal found?

The largest deposits of bituminous coal in the U.S. are in the eastern and east central states. One vast deposit ranges southwestward from Pennsylvania through Ohio, West Virginia, Virginia, eastern Kentucky, and Tennessee to northern Alabama. The second major coal-producing area covers the states of Illinois, Indiana, and western Kentucky.

Eight states in the High Plains have large deposits of bituminous and subbituminous coal and lignite. These are Utah, Wyoming, Montana, North and South Dakota, Colorado, Arizona, and New Mexico. Among them, they produced 202 million tons of coal in 1980, of which 89 percent was surface-mined. Only 21.6 million tons came from deep mines.

About 70 percent of the coal mined in the United States comes from east of the Mississippi, but eastern states contain only 45 percent of the nation's total bituminous, subbituminous, and lignite reserves.

What factors comprise the "quality" of coal?

The quality of coal receives much attention from electric companies. Apart from the sulfur content, important because of air pollution considerations, numerous other coal quality factors are critical to power plant performance. These qualities include heating value (Btu content), ash content, composition, fusion temperature, and engineering properties, such as grindability. These factors are critical in determining whether coal can be used in a particular generating plant.

Is there a difference between eastern and western coal?

Western coal, on the average, has a much lower sulfur content—some of it as low as 0.6 to 0.7 percent by weight—than eastern coal, much of which is in the 2.0 to 4.0 percent sulfur range. The greater the sulfur content of coal, the greater the amount of sulfur dioxide gas, an air pollutant, produced when the coal is burned. Thus, low sulfur western coal allows utilities and industrial users to meet strict government standards on sulfur emissions more efficiently.

On the other hand, western coal has a lower Btu rate, or heat-producing ability, than eastern coal. This means that more western coal must be burned to produce the same amount of heat that eastern coal can produce.

HOW IS COAL PRODUCED?

Sixty percent of the nation's coal is produced by surface or strip mining, from seams fairly close to the surface. In this method, earth and rock above the coal seam—the overburden—are removed and placed to one side, exposing the coal. After the coal is removed, the overburden is regraded to the desired shape and topsoil is replaced. Vegetation or young trees are planted, and the land is restored to productive use as pasture, farmland, or recreation area.

In other instances, surface mining is not the best technique for extracting coal from the earth. Tunnels must be dug deep underground to reach the coal that then is removed by one of several possible methods. Under one method, called conventional mining, explosives are inserted into the coal. When they are set off, the coal breaks into pieces and is removed from the mine. In another method, called continuous mining, a machine is used to cut through the coal and load it for removal. Some coal is left to support the roof. Under the longwall method, coal is removed in a similar way, but roof supports are not used. Instead, the roof is supported by hydraulic jacks that are moved along with the cutting machine, allowing the roof to cave in after the coal is extracted.

What about the environmental effects of mining?

Surface mining and deep mining can pose unique environmental problems. While surface mining has proven to be fast and efficient, with a high percentage of coal recovery, the correction of its after-effects has long concerned both government and the coal industry. Many states have had laws for some time that regulate the reclamation process and minimize surface mining's impact on the environment. In 1977, the U.S. Congress set minimum standards for both surface and underground operations. The federal act imposes strict controls on surface coal mining, unless the states already apply standards that are at least as strict. Costs of complying with the act have been reflected in the prices consumers pay.

One environmental problem associated with the deep-mining process is acid mine water. Depending on geographic conditions and depth, water seeps into deep mines, sometimes flooding them, and must be pumped out. Acid mine drainage is formed by the reaction of oxygen and water with the pyrite (iron sulfide) in the coal. If present in large enough concentrations, the acid produced by the reaction may contaminate the mine water and, consequently, the bodies of water into which it is pumped. To pinpoint where such problems may arise, scientists utilize infrared photography and chemical tracers to track down acid formations.

In existing mines, acid drainage is controlled by treating the water before it is released. In most instances, the treatment involves neutralization with lime and settling to reduce the concentration of iron.

Efforts are underway to remove other constituents of mine drainage. Bituminous Coal Research, Inc., the research arm of the National Coal Association, has been in the forefront of mine drainage research, along with the Environmental Protection Agency, the Appalachian Regional Commission, several universities, and state agencies.

What is being done to restore previously mined lands?

Although presently operating surface mines must pay careful attention under federal and state law to restoring the land, the scars of earlier mining operations are still visible in a few instances. Under law, every ton of coal sold must include in its price a fee to be used to restore these older abandoned mines.

Many coal operators have developed methods to minimize the amount of land affected by mining, using as a foundation the fundamental concept "the less land disturbed, the less to reclaim." Speedy and hardy vegetation is a cornerstone of successful reclamation, and researchers have continued to search for quicker and better ways "to re-green" mined land. Extensive experiments have been conducted with all-season seeding. Traditionally, the planting season has been confined to the spring months, with occasional seedings in the fall. Now, researchers are recommending seeding within 15 days of grading, no matter what the month, unless weather conditions are truly impossible.

By seeding a mixture of annuals and perennials, it is possible for reclaimers to establish some early ground cover that minimizes runoff, erosion, and compaction. Then, reseeding can be performed again in the spring or fall to enhance the first growth.

Much research also has been conducted in identifying and evaluating the various strata of overburden. Early identification of soil characteristics allows for careful preplanning that makes best use of the growing medium.

One forestry program plants alternate rows of fast-, medium-, and slow-growth trees. As the faster growing species mature and are harvested, the slow-growth hardwoods have room to take over.

Forest planting is only one of many alternative uses for mined land. Others, such as farms, recreation areas, orchards, and housing developments, have been enormously successful. The decision about which of these options to select depends on the soil and weather conditions, the general terrain, and the needs of the surrounding community.

How long does it take and how much does it cost to open a new deep mine?

Starting a new underground mine is an expensive and time-consuming process. To develop a new deep mine that produces two million tons a year with a 20-to-30-year life span can require five to seven years and an investment of $100 million or more. Mine expansion is similarly time-consuming and costly.

What new techniques are being used to improve mine productivity?

Research is being conducted to develop more sophisticated equipment, incorporating the use of computers and other modern technologies into the mining operation. These include automatic extraction systems that control every aspect of coal removal and transfer, improved automated and closed-wall longwall equipment, automated remote-controlled and water-jet continuous miners, automated continuous roof supports, underground augering, and high-speed boring of mine tunnels and main entries.

What about the health and safety of miners?

Health and safety are paramount concerns in coal mining. State and federal laws and regulations, such as the U.S. Coal Mine Health and Safety Act, as well as company safety rules, impose elaborate safety precautions on every phase of mining. Company officials make health and safety inspections daily. In addition, federal and state agencies conduct extensive inspections. Federal inspectors made more than 109,000 inspections at some 5,761 coal mines and related facilites in 1980. Mining states also conduct mine inspections.

The air in each underground working area is tested for dust, and each miner must wear a personal air sampler at regular intervals. The federal government reported 74 percent of 5,015 working sections in underground mines had dust levels in the period from Oct. 1, 1979 to Sept. 30, 1980 of no more than two milligrams per cubic meter. Medical authorities agree concentrations of dust this low are not harmful.

Accidents are always a concern, but U.S. mines today are safer places to work than they ever have been. The number of fatal accidents has fallen each year since 1970, and in 1980 occurred at the rate of 0.3 per million man-hours worked, the lowest rate ever. Coal operators, miners, and the government continue to review problem areas to improve the working environment.

What is a "captive mine"?

Since the future adequacy and reliability of electricity supplies will depend to a great extent on a stable and secure supply of coal, many utilities have been relying more heavily on long-term contracts for coal supplies. Approximately 88.5 percent of the coal delivered to utilities in 1980 was purchased under contract rather than on the spot market. A growing number are going into the mining business to produce coal for their own needs (captive coal). Captive coal deliveries in 1978 equaled about 67.1 million tons, or about 14 percent of the 476.2 million tons consumed that year. The Federal Energy Regulatory Commission predicts that captive coal mines will account for about 20 percent of the market in 1985. Currently, there are 82 utilities mining coal or holding coal reserves.

HOW IS COAL TRANSPORTED?

Coal transportation accounts for a significant share of the nation's commodity traffic. About 65 percent of the coal produced in the United States leaves the mine by rail. Barges carry about 10 percent and trucks about 13 percent. About 2 percent is used at the mine, and 10 percent is moved by conveyor belt or truck to mine-mouth generating plants. These plants transmit coal's energy to distant population centers via high-voltage transmission lines. In a very real sense, electricity customers receive "coal by wire."

How much coal do railroads move?

Railroads hauled about 535 million tons of coal in 1980 for at least part of the journey to consumers, which include power plants, factories, and other industrial facilities. The amount of coal hauled by rail exceeds that of any other commodity. In 1980, coal movements generated about $5 billion in revenue for the nation's railroads.

What is a unit train?

Much of the coal hauled by rail moves in unit trains—typically 100 cars—each with a 100-ton capacity. These long strings of high capacity coal cars are never uncoupled and generally shuttle between one coal mine and one power plant. Many of these trains need to stop only for servicing and fresh crews. They take on their loads while moving under a chute at the mine, and dump the coal at the power plant while just slowing down.

Unit trains now move much of all the coal hauled by the major railroads. They eliminate needless switching and delay and use coal cars more efficiently, enabling the railroads to offer lower rates for unit train coal movements. More efficiency makes the coal cost less, of course—a saving that directly benefits electricity consumers.

What role do barges play in moving coal?

Water carriers move mountains of coal. Barges carry more coal than any other commodity, about 22 percent of the total traffic. In recent years, barge lines and inland ports invested millions of dollars in sophisticated coal-handling facilities and equipment, and the capacity of barges has increased greatly where they are not limited by the size of river locks. A single tow of up to 20 barges can carry 20,000 to 30,000 tons.

Towboats of improved power and design move such clusters of coal cargo along inland waterways at low cost. Coal is a major item of traffic along the Ohio River and its tributaries. Coal also moves down the Mississippi, and large tonnages are transferred near the river mouth to ocean-going barges which cross the Gulf of Mexico to power plants in Florida. Barge lines also are linked to rail loading points in an efficient, integrated transportation network, so coal that moves part of the way to market by water may finish the trip by rail. In 1980, 135.5 million tons were moved on the nation's inland waterways.

The Great Lakes are another highway for coal. Lake Erie ports such as Toledo and Sandusky receive coal, often by unit train, and load it into freighters for consumers in Canada or for U.S. destinations on the upper lakes. Ports such as Duluth, MN handle coal shipments from the western U.S. destined for Chicago and Detroit. In addition, about two million tons are loaded each year at Great Lakes ports for export overseas.

How are trucks used to move coal?

Trucks often are used to deliver coal to locations when other forms of transportation cannot be used, to carry coal for short distances, and to make connections with trains and barges. Usually they carry coal for distances of less than 50 miles.

What is a "mine-mouth" plant?

The alternative to delivering coal to market is to bring the market to the coal. This happens in the case of mine-mouth power plants—generating plants built as close as possible to the coal mine.

A cluster of these generating plants in western Pennsylvania, for example, sends power to markets as distant as New York City, using 500,000-volt lines. The cost of that power to consumers is less than it would be if the coal had to be transported. Other mine-mouth power plants in West Virginia, Kentucky, Ohio, and other states use coal from nearby mines to generate power for distant markets.

What is a coal slurry pipeline?

A coal slurry pipeline is a facility for transporting coal. First the coal is crushed into a powdery form, then mixed with water, and finally pumped through a pipeline. The "slurry" is the thick soup of water and finely ground coal. Because of its lower operating costs, the fact that it can be hidden underground, and its ability to operate without having to haul empty cars back to the mine, a slurry pipeline can have economic advantages over other forms of transportation.

Slurry pipelines, however, require a considerable amount of water to transport the coal. This required water supply in the arid western regions, where most of the proposed pipelines would originate, will be a major obstacle in their development. In addition to the water supply problem, slurry pipeline developers must acquire a continuous strip of land, perhaps 1,000 miles in length, for the pipeline right-of-way.

The technology for pumping coal and water is not new. The first patent for a slurry pipeline was issued in 1891, and by 1914 a line was carrying coal into London. Years passed, however, before the technology began to spread.

In 1957, a 108-mile line was built to carry coal to a power plant near Cleveland, Ohio. It was operated for five years but was put in mothballs when lower rates were posted by the railroads. A longer version was built later from a mine in northeastern Arizona across 273 miles of mountain and desert. It has been used since 1971 to transport fuel to the Mohave generating stations at the southern tip of Nevada. This is the only slurry pipeline currently in operation in the United States.

Nine additional pipelines have been proposed in the United States. They would carry western coal to the South, the Southwest, and the Pacific Northwest, and eastern and midwestern coal to the South and East Coast. Four of the proposed pipelines would each carry more than 20 million tons of coal yearly. The most advanced proposed pipeline would carry 25 million tons of Wyoming coal a year more than 1,000 miles to utilities in Arkansas and points along the Mississippi.

HOW IS COAL USED TO PRODUCE ELECTRICITY?

Coal is the major fuel for electricity generation, and is increasing in importance as utilities seek to decrease their reliance on more expensive, less available fuels—such as oil. Of the 699 million tons of coal consumed in the United States in 1980, approximately 81 percent was burned to make electricity. Industrial and retail users consumed about 9 percent, and about 10 percent was coking coal used by the steel industry. In addition, 90 million tons of coal were exported.

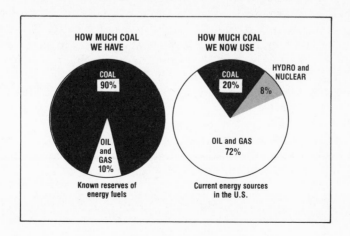

HOW MUCH COAL WE HAVE

COAL 90%

OIL and GAS 10%

Known reserves of energy fuels

HOW MUCH COAL WE NOW USE

COAL 20%

HYDRO and NUCLEAR 8%

OIL and GAS 72%

Current energy sources in the U.S.

When is coal ready for use?

As coal leaves the mine, it may contain bits of rock and other impurities that were imbedded in the seam or picked up in the mining process. About half the coal produced in the United States goes through a crushing, sizing, washing, drying, and treatment process at a preparation plant, usually located near the mine mouth. Some coal customers, however, find it more economic to use run-of-mine coal if they have boilers designed to burn raw coal and are permitted to do so.

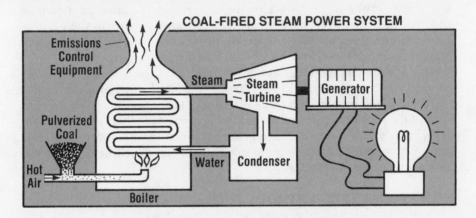

COAL-FIRED STEAM POWER SYSTEM

Emissions Control Equipment · Steam · Steam Turbine · Generator · Pulverized Coal · Hot Air · Water · Condenser · Boiler

How does a power plant receive and burn coal?

In a "fossil-fuel" power plant, coal, oil, or gas burned in a furnace provides heat to change water to steam. The steam turns the blades of a turbine that spins a generator, producing electricity.

The coal delivered to a coal-fired power plant is first placed in a storage area. When it is needed to generate electricity, it is transported to a "crusher," a machine that reduces the size of the coal pieces to an average of three-quarters of an inch. Next, the coal is transported to a pulverizing mill where it is ground to the consistency of face powder for efficient burning. It is then mixed with air and burned in the boiler. The heat from the burning coal is transferred to water that circulates in a closed cycle in pipes around the boiler, changing the water to steam. The steam is used to turn a turbine that is connected to an electric generator.

A device called a "feeder" controls the amount of coal that enters the mill and the boiler. This control is very important in the operation of an electric generating unit because the generation of electric energy is a matter of rather delicate balance. The heat required to produce the steam that drives the generator must produce the exact number of kilowatts needed at that precise time. The accelerator on a car regulates speed in much the same way.

The electricity generator is designed to run at a constant speed. When more load (demand for power) is coming on the generator, which is like

74

going uphill in a car, the coal feeder has to let in more fuel, just as the accelerator on a car lets in more gasoline when it is pressed down. The amount of coal has to be matched by an increase in the amount of combustion air to produce the right amount of steam. When load is being reduced on the generator, less coal and air have to be fed into the boiler (like taking one's foot off the accelerator) so there won't be too much heat. If all these factors do not balance properly in a generating plant, the generator "trips out," or shuts down. Unless the electric company can cover this loss in electricity supply, customers might have a power interruption. As a result, companies are motivated to have only highly trained and qualified "drivers," that is, power plant operators and engineers.

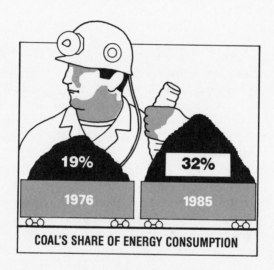

COAL'S SHARE OF ENERGY CONSUMPTION

How much electricity comes from coal?

In 1970, coal-generated electricity was 46 percent of total U.S. utility electricity production. In 1980 it was 51 percent. The amount of coal used to produce electric power during the same period increased from 319 million tons to an estimated 568 million tons in 1980. The President's 1981 National Energy Plan predicts coal's share of "total" energy consumed in the United States will grow from less than 19 percent in 1976 to nearly 32 percent by 1985, and total production will rise to about one billion tons.

Here are some examples of how much coal is used yearly to produce the electricity for operation of various appliances:

Electric water heater — two tons of coal for a family of four.

Range — A half-ton of coal for a family of four.

Clothes dryer — A half-ton of coal.

Color television (tube type) — A half-ton of coal.

It takes about one ton of coal to produce 2,000 kilowatt-hours of electricity. Checking the number of kilowatt-hours used during a billing period will show a consumer how many pounds of coal were used to meet his needs (presuming all the power was coal-generated.)

WHAT ABOUT THE ENVIRONMENTAL IMPACTS OF USING COAL?

The electric utility industry believes that by increasing its reliance on coal for generating electricity, it can help insure that American consumers will receive a reliable electricity supply at the lowest possible costs. It recognizes, at the same time, that (1) adequate environmental controls to protect the public health are essential and (2) regulations that achieve a reasonable balance between environmental goals and energy needs will benefit both utilities and their customers.

Can more coal be used without endangering public health or the environment?

The U.S. Department of Health, Education and Welfare reported on January 16, 1978 that "intensified use of coal as an energy source as proposed in the President's national energy plan would not lead to serious health or ecological consequences, if certain precautions are taken." They are being taken.

What about air pollution?

The same rich chemical composition that makes coal such a valuable resource also contributes an undesirable effect—it creates by-products during combustion that, in sufficient quantity, can pose environmental problems. The two major by-products, particulate matter and sulfur dioxide, have been areas of environmental concern for several years.

Particulate emissions from power plants come primarily from the unburnable materials in the coal, called ash. Currently, federal regulations require that more than 99 percent of the ash particles be cleaned from the combustion gases before the gases are allowed to go up the chimney and into the atmosphere. Because so little of the particulate material is allowed to enter the atmosphere, coal-burning power plants do not contribute significantly to the particulate material in the air around us.

Sulfur dioxide is formed during the burning of coal by the combination of the sulfur present in coal with the oxygen in the air. The industry has researched the health effects of sulfur oxides for decades. It now appears that sulfur dioxide gas itself is not a major health concern. Major human medical studies and other experiments have not shown a direct link between sulfur dioxide and irreversible health damage. It is now thought, however, that the adherence of sulfur dioxide and sulfates to fine particulates could cause health damage. These particulates also may contain small amounts of other toxic materials.

The Electric Power Research Institute (EPRI) has underway extensive studies to determine whether sulfur/particulate compounds affect health. EPRI is conducting studies on people who are exposed occupationally to

76

these compounds, and on animals in controlled environments. In addition, the Institute is studying what happens to sulfur dioxide after it leaves the stack, how it becomes associated with particulates, and to what extent people are exposed to these compounds.

How is particulate matter controlled?

Particulate matter is removed from the combustion gases primarily by cleaning the gas with an "electrostatic precipitator" or filtering it in a "baghouse."

When the gases from burning coal are passed through an electrostatic precipitator, the particles of dust and ash are given an electrical charge. This charge allows the particles to be drawn off, as if by a magnet, and collected rather than discharged into the atmosphere.

A baghouse on a power plant operates in a manner very similar to a household vacuum cleaner. The combustion gases are passed through a series of filter bags that trap the particles of dust and ash. Periodically, the bags are shaken in such a manner that the material collected falls into a collecting bin where it can be removed.

How is sulfur dioxide controlled?

Sulfur dioxide is controlled through the following methods:

a) burning coal with a low sulfur content;
b) removing some of the sulfur from the coal before it is burned; and
c) cleaning the sulfur dioxide out of the combustion gases before they are allowed to enter the atmosphere.

Certain types of coal, found primarily in the western states such as Montana and Wyoming and in some eastern states, contain much less sulfur than is found in the higher-sulfur types of coal that many utilities use. Burning these types of low-sulfur coal will reduce sulfur dioxide emissions by 75 to 80 percent when compared with higher-sulfur coals. Unfortunately, because of the locations of the low-sulfur supplies, in many cases the coal cannot be transported efficiently to all the areas that would want to use it.

An alternative to buying low-sulfur coal is to clean some of the sulfur out of the coal before it is burned. This is possible because the sulfur in the coal exists in two forms—organic and pyritic. Organic sulfur is combined chemically within the structure of the coal itself and, unfortunately, cannot be separated physically. Pyritic sulfur, however, exists as separate particles within the coal. Crushing the coal frees these particles and the majority of them can be separated from the coal through a process involving washing, screening, and filtering. This process involves complex equipment and produces considerable waste material that must be disposed of in an environmentally acceptable manner. Depending on the type of coal, approximately 15 to 25 percent of the sulfur in the coal may be removed by this process with a corresponding reduction in sulfur dioxide emissions.

The third alternative, cleaning the sulfur dioxide out of the combustion gases, involves the use of a device commonly known as a scrubber. Though there are different types currently in use, they all operate on the same basic principle: passing the combustion gases through a chemical solution, a process known as "washing" the gases. During the washing process, the sulfur dioxide gas reacts with the chemicals in the solution to form a new substance. This substance can either be filtered out of the combustion gas, in the case of a "dry" scrubber, or separated from the used chemical solution in the case of a "wet" scrubber.

The amount of waste material or sludge produced by a scrubber can be considerable, especially in the case of a wet scrubber. Studies are underway to evaluate possible uses of this waste material. However, for the foreseeable future, the majority of the sludge produced by scrubbers will have to be disposed of as a landfill material. The disposal problem is one of the major concerns of scrubber operation because of the large volume of material that must be handled and the care that must be taken in disposing of the sludge in an environmentally acceptable manner.

Because scrubbers remove sulfur dioxide after it has formed, their efficiency and reliability are important considerations. Current experience and technology indicates that recently designed scrubbers typically can remove 75 percent or more of the sulfur dioxide from the combustion gases. During the time a scrubber is not operating, current federal regulations generally require that the power plant be shut down or its output be restricted to protect air quality.

What is the economic impact of air pollution controls?

Federal regulations require sulfur dioxide scrubbers and extremely efficient particulate controls on all new power plants. While these two devices are not the only air pollution controls installed at a power plant, they are the most significant. Together, they may add anywhere from 20 to 35 percent to the cost of building a power plant. That cost, of course, ultimately will show up in consumers' bills. In addition, the sulfur dioxide and particulate control devices will use between three-and-a-half and five-and-a-half percent of the electricity produced by the plant just to operate the pumps, fans, and other equipment associated with these devices.

The costs of complying with environmental standards can vary significantly, depending on such factors as where a plant is located, what type of coal is being burned, and what type of equipment is being installed. National Economic Research Associates estimates these costs will reach $12 billion a year in 1990.

What is "acid rain"?

All precipitation—rain, snow, sleet, fog, hail, or dew—is acidic to some degree. The level of acidity is what determines whether the precipitation is referred to as "acid rain."

Scientists measure acidity and its opposite, alkalinity, on a pH scale. The most alkaline scale measurement is pH 14; the most acid is pH 0, and the neutral point is pH 7.0. Acid rain generally is defined as rain whose acidity is lower than pH 5.6, although the range of acidity in natural rainfall may be substantially lower. Acid compounds also may settle to the ground in dry form. These dry acidic deposits may be referred to as acid rain, too.

As the result of various natural phenomena, such as volcanoes and sea spray, and of man's activities, such as the burning of coal and oil, oxides of sulfur and nitrogen are discharged into the atmosphere. Some of these natural and man-made emissions undergo a series of chemical reactions and eventually may be converted into the sulfates and nitrates that have been identified in acid rain. Unfortunately, these chemical reactions, the amounts and types of emissions, and the controlling factors affecting the process are not understood very well.

What do we know about the causes and effects of acid rain?

This is the question scientists in government, industry, and the academic world are struggling to answer. Scientists have demonstrated that a number of lakes—a few of which are located in the Adirondack Mountains, for example—are susceptible to acidification as the direct result of acid rain. However, other evidence is not yet available. We know, in general, that acidity occurs in precipitation and in environmental systems such as lakes, rivers, forests, and soils. We don't know to what extent they are related.

Is rain becoming more acidic?

The United States now has developed high quality acid rain monitoring networks. We do not have, unfortunately, a good historical data base concerning acid rain and, therefore, cannot determine past trends to be used for comparison. Of the data that is available, the longest continuous record of precipitation chemistry in the United States has been compiled at Hubbard Brook, a research station in north central New Hampshire. Data that have been collected there since 1963 show fluctuations in rain pH from week to week and from year to year. No long term trends, however, can be found either in the charted annual averages or in statistical analyses of weekly readings.

Much more information is needed to determine the roles of utility coal burning, industrial activities, or motor vehicle operation in the development of acid rain. And, prediction of what sort of rain acidity will result from a particular mix of pollutants currently is not possible.

All facets of the acid rain issue need further scientific study and evidence to develop a sound basis for future decision making. The electric utility industry and federal, state, and local governments are conducting such research.

WHAT IS BEING DONE TO MAKE ELECTRICITY PRODUCTION FROM COAL CLEANER AND MORE EFFICIENT?

Nearly all experts point to coal as one of the few near-term alternatives with significant potential for electric power production. Projections show that in 1990 about 77 percent of all the coal consumed in the United States most likely will be used by the electric power industry.

Although most generating plants at that time probably will still be directly firing pulverized coal, a broad array of new technologies are being developed and readied to use coal both efficiently and in a more assuredly clean manner. These may include fluidized-bed combustion (to capture sulfur ahead of the exhaust stack), coal liquefaction (to produce liquid fuel from coal), coal gasification integrated with combined cycles (converting coal to a low or intermediate Btu gas and then extracting its energy through gas and steam turbines in tandem), and coal processing (such as solvent-refined coal). Each of these technologies offers different performance and economic incentives.

How is the electric utility industry investigating coal-cleaning processes?

The industry is increasing its efforts to find economical, efficient methods for cleaning coal before it is burned in power plants. The most advanced coal cleaning plant ever constructed, called The Coal Cleaning Test Facility, recently began operating in Homer City, PA. The facility is sponsored by the Electric Power Research Institute, Pennsylvania Electric Co., New York State Electric and Gas Corp., and the Empire State Electric Energy Research Corp. EPRI is examining methods for cleaning various types of coal and for lowering the costs of the cleaning processes. Tests to characterize completely the cleanability limits of steam coal will begin in March, 1982. The facility also is used as a training center for industry personnel involved in preparing and cleaning coal for use in power plants. Data will be gathered on newly developed as well as conventional coal cleaning methods.

What is fluidized-bed combustion?

Fluidized-bed combustion has potential for making possible the greater use of high-sulfur coal. In a fluidized-bed boiler, particles of coal are suspended in a stream of air blowing upward through a bed of ash and limestone heated to about 1,600 degrees. Crushed coal injected into the combustion zone with limestone burns very rapidly. Calcium in the limestone reacts with sulfur dioxide released from the burning coal, producing calcium sulfate, an inert substance discharged with the coal ash.

Fluidized-bed systems remove not only most pyritic sulfur, but also the organic sulfur that is contained in coal. In addition, recent EPRI studies have shown a major reduction in nitrous oxide formation during coal burning.

Compared with conventional coal-fired boilers, fluidized-bed systems offer higher power generation efficiencies and cleaner exhaust gases. If the fluidized bed is operated under pressure, additional economies are possible through decreased construction requirements and lower operating costs.

As promising as the fluidized-bed system is, it is still expensive, at least in terms of initial costs. These systems were offered for commercial sale in small industrial sizes for the first time in 1977, and could be in wide use by the end of this century.

What is coal liquefaction?

EPRI, the federal government, and private industry have built an "H-Coal" pilot plant that is designed to convert up to 250 tons of coal a day to distillate oil and up to 600 tons a day to heavy boiler oil. The plant, which began operating in the spring of 1980, is located in Cattlettsburg, KY. The electric utility industry is vitally concerned with this process because petroleum fuels are going to become less available and the industry is dependent on petroleum for certain generating uses.

When the pilot plant has completed two to three years of operation, researchers hope to have the information necessary to increase the scale to a 30,000 ton-a-day commercial coal refinery. The pilot plant is based on commercial designs and equipment currently used in petroleum refineries, so none of the the equipment will be difficult to translate to commercial size.

Another liquefaction plant, using the Exxon Donor Solvent process, has been built and is operating in Baytown, TX. Again, the objective is development of the engineering information necessary to build a full-scale plant.

What is coal gasification?

Coal gasification is a process by which coal is turned into a gas. Some technologies for doing this have been known and used for many years, but the gas they produce is expensive. Now, with natural gas becoming more expensive, there is renewed interest in developing new means for transforming coal into gas.

The most efficient way for utilities to utilize the gas produced from coal would be in a combined-cycle system, which joins together two means of producing electricity. First, electricity is produced by burning the coal gas in a combustion turbine, similar to an aircraft jet engine, that is connected to a generator. The hot exhaust gases leaving the combustion turbine are then piped to a conventional boiler where their heat is used to produce steam. This steam then is used to turn a steam turbine connected to a second generator.

A combined-cycle coal gasification system has the potential of producing electricity from coal less expensively than any other system, but, at this stage of development, the actual costs are not known. A combined-cycle gasification plant may be cost-competitive with standard pulverized coal boilers encumbered with necessary sulfur oxide, particulate, and NO_x controls.

Engineering design work is well underway on a 100-megawatt coal gasifier/combined-cycle demonstration project to be located at Southern California Edison Co.'s Cool Water site in Daggett, CA. The plant is expected to begin operating in 1984. The project is designed to determine whether such a system can be made to operate, what kinds of engineering changes are going to have to be made to coal gasifiers and to combined cycle units, what kinds of pollution control equipment will have to be installed, and how they will integrate into utility systems. The potential of such a project is very great, but so are the uncertainties.

What is solvent refining?

One of the newest techniques to control the environmental effects of burning coal is solvent refining. One such process, called SRC-I, has been tested successfully and is ready to be used in the first commercial-size plant.

In this refining process, coal is mixed with a solvent in a hydrogen-rich atmosphere at about 825 degrees Fahrenheit. Sulfur in the coal is released as hydrogen sulfide gas—and this gas can be recovered and converted to elemental sulfur for industrial use. Ash and insoluble matter from the coal (which is now in liquid form) settle during the process, leaving the refined coal. When cooled it becomes a brittle, shiny solid that can be transported and easily handled in facilities designed for coal.

A wide variety of different coal types can be refined in this manner. The refined fuel has a value of 16,000 Btu per pound in contrast to the 8,000 to 12,000 Btu for the original coal. The sulfur content of the refined coal generally would be about 0.6 to 0.8 percent. Another variation of the solvent refining process produces a liquid rather than a solid fuel as its end product.

What are some of the other technologies being studied to provide clean, efficient burning of coal?

A long-term possibility is the magnetohydrodynamic (MHD) system. In this process, coal and preheated air are fired in a burner at very high temperatures. Potassium salts are added, producing a gas of high conductivity. The gas is then passed through a magnetic field, producing electricity. The hot gases are exhausted to a steam boiler.

How soon will new technologies have an impact?

It takes about 30 to 40 years for a new technology to advance from the concept stage to use on a significant scale in the electric utility industry and, for that matter, in just about any other industry. First, the new technology's feasibility must be demonstrated by laboratory testing. Next, scientists must determine whether the technology can be applied on a practical basis. During the next stage—commercialization—investors must decide whether they want to use their money to order the equipment. Finally, the technology must prove economically competitive; that is, offer a product or service customers will buy.

The maximum rate at which any new power generation technology might be integrated into the existing system can be illustrated by assuming the successful operation of a pilot plant by 1980 and the completion of a large demonstration plant by 1985. Consider the following additional assumptions:

1. Capacity growth of 5 percent per year.
2. New plant construction time of eight years.
3. More than 20 percent of all plant orders are of the new type even before the first commercial unit begins operation in 1990.
4. One-half of all new plants ordered after 1993 employ the new technology.

With this extremely optimistic scenario, the new technology would supply only about 8.2 percent of the nation's electricity in the year 2000. If a 10-year construction time is assumed (instead of eight years) the new technology would provide only 5.3 percent of the electricity in the year 2000.

WHAT IS THE FUTURE OF COAL?

Even though coal is a relatively abundant energy source, demand for it has increased slowly. Demand rates, however, are expected to increase as the nation seeks to reduce its dependence on foreign oil supplies and to keep energy costs as low as possible. Coal demand increases averaged less than three percent annually through 1977. Since then they have increased an average of 4.8 percent a year. A National Coal Association (NCA) study predicts that in the next ten years demand will increase from 3.6 percent to 6.9 percent annually.

Can the coal industry meet increased demand?

Barring unreasonable governmental or legal delays in the opening of new mines, particularly surface mines in the West, the coal industry will have sufficient mining capacity to meet demand over the next decades. The NCA says coal production most likely will reach more than one billion tons in 1985 and 1.35 billion tons in 1990, compared with the 824 million tons produced in 1980. The NCA estimates the industry has the capacity to mine from 100 million to 150 million tons more coal per year than is currently being used.

From almost every indication, sufficient mining capacity is being planned to meet the needs of the electric utility industry, the largest coal consumer in the United States. Electric utilities used 568 million tons of coal in 1980. A 1981 National Electric Reliability Council study estimates electric utility coal consumption will reach 684 million tons in 1985 and almost 881 million tons in 1990.

Because of the tremendous capital investment required to construct electric plants, much of the coal supplied to utility customers, almost 80 percent, is purchased under long-term contracts. (It would make little sense to have an expensive generating plant sitting idle for want of fuel.) The construction time for new power plants is generally longer than for the coal mines needed to supply them, allowing the coal industry sufficient time to secure coal reserves, sign contracts, and begin the construction of new mines.

To meet the needs of utilities and other customers, the nation's coal companies plan to open or expand 324 new mines by 1989. They could produce about 819.7 million tons of coal annually. These new and expanded mines will increase overall coal production and also compensate for the depletion of old mines.

Adequate manpower is expected to be available, although there are no certain answers to the coal industry's labor problems. The experience of recent years has shown thousands of new miners can be brought into the industry each year. Many challenges must be faced in training and developing new manpower, but the coal industry is devoting increasing attention to this area and has met with success.

In the long run, the amount of coal that can be produced depends greatly on leasing of federally-owned coal deposits, mainly in the West. Today, only about 75 million tons a year come from these lands. There has been a freeze on new federal leasing since 1971.

Will the nation's transportation system be able to handle future coal needs?

Since railroads are expected to transport most of the increased coal supply in future years, they will need to make substantial capital investments. To haul the additional tonnage projected for the nation's energy needs and to replace older cars used for existing coal movement, the railroads estimate they must acquire 10,160 to 14,700 coal cars annually for the next four years, depending on the type of trains used.

This goal is manageable, they say, because the time it takes to obtain rail equipment is considerably less than the time it takes to bring new mines into production or to construct an electric generating plant. The railroads' most serious problems are deteriorating or inadequate roadbeds. New and heavier tracks, centralized traffic control, and other improvements are needed in some parts of the country to allow the railroads to increase capacity.

Expanded mining of the vast reserves of low-sulfur coal in the West will generate dramatic increases in rail coal traffic in that region. Western railroads, as a result, are anticipating much greater investment in their physical plant than railroads in other coal regions already in greater production. Western coal now accounts for about 30 percent of annual coal output. But the West probably will supply nearly 40 percent of the total in 1990.

Some Westerners worry about the effects of increased traffic through the small towns lying in the path of coal train movement. They fear these towns could become clogged and disrupted by repeated intrusion of trains many times a day. In some areas, alleviating the impact of the coal train traffic will require installing above-grade crossings, relocating railroads or streets and highways, constructing double track, and other measures. These are problems that can be solved, but large sums of money may be needed.

While barges and ships will continue to transport a substantial portion of coal, expansion of this transportation form is hindered by the limited number of suitable waterways. Nevertheless, the barge industry believes its fleet can be expanded to handle increased coal shipments in the years ahead. Barge operators do foresee problems with certain waterways because of inadequate lock and dam structures and other physical constraints such as channel depth and width.

Trucks serve as a vital form of coal transportation. Their high cost and dependence on oil for fuel, however, means they probably will not be used to carry a major portion of future coal supply.

Slurry pipelines have great potential for playing a major role in future coal transportation. A 1978 federal government study said such pipelines can be a preferable transportation form in certain instances, such as when coal must be moved long distances from a single mine to a single destination and other transportation methods are not available. Development of coal slurry pipelines has been hindered, however, by factors such as the opposition of railroads and by unresolved issues—for example, the usage of water in western regions of the country.

HOW MUCH COAL IS NEEDED TO PROVIDE ELECTRICITY FOR COMMON HOUSEHOLD APPLIANCES?

It's apparent how crucial coal supplies are when some common household uses of electricity are translated into pounds of coal.

The table below shows how much coal would be burned to operate these appliances in one home for one year, presuming average use.

Appliance	Average Wattage	Est. Pounds* of Coal Consumed Annually
Broiler	1,140	85
Dishwasher	1,201	363
Oven, microwave (only)	1,450	190
Range		
with oven	12,200	700
with self-cleaning oven	12,200	730
Clothes Dryer	4,856	993
Iron (hand)	1,100	60
Washing Machine		
(automatic)	512	103
Washing Machine		
(non-automatic)	286	76
Water Heater	2,475	4,219
(quick-recovery)	4,474	4,811
Refrigerators/Freezers		
manual defrost, 12.5 cu. ft.	—	1,500
automatic defrost, 17.5 cu. ft.	—	2,250
Hair Dryer	600	25
Television		
black & white		
tube type	100	220
solid state	45	100
color		
tube type	240	528
solid state	145	320
Clock	2	17
Vacuum Cleaner	630	46

*One kilowatt hour of electricity uses nearly one pound of coal

SOURCES

Numerous scientific and informational sources were used to produce this chapter. In addition to Edison Electric Institute, the sources include several federal agencies, the National Coal Association, Iowa Electric Light and Power Company, Ohio Edison Company, Chemical Engineering Magazine, Panhandle Magazine, Industry Week Magazine, the Electric Power Research Institute, the Coal Policy Project, and coal and transportation firms.

WHERE TO CALL

Additional information on coal and answers to questions are available from the following government agencies and private organizations:

Bituminous Coal Research, Inc.
Monroeville, PA 412/327-1600

National Coal Association
Washington, DC 202/463-2625

Edison Electric Institute
Washington, DC 202/828-7400

U.S. Department of Energy
Office of Public Affairs
Washington, DC 202/252-5568

U.S. Department of Interior
Bureau of Mines
Washington, DC 202/634-1004

The electric company that provides service in your area.

ALTERNATIVE ENERGY SOURCES AND TECHNOLOGIES

ANSWERS TO YOUR QUESTIONS

ELECTRIC ENERGY: AN INTRODUCTION

Energy is the source of all activity, growth, and change in our world. The demand for electric energy in particular is growing faster than for any other energy form. Because of technological and financial constraints, the electric utility industry will have to rely to a large degree on traditional methods and fuels to meet demand increases in future years. But the industry is committed to tapping the potential of alternative energy sources and is involved directly in efforts to research and develop them. This booklet presents an overview of alternative electric power production technologies—both currently available and under research—with which traditional sources and technologies can be supplemented.

Today, about one-third of our energy is converted into electricity before it is used. By the end of this century, almost half of our energy consumption is expected to be in the form of electricity. Expected increases in electricity consumption are part of a long-term trend. In 1960, for example, the average residential electric customer used 3,854 kilowatt-hours of electricity a year. Since then, average annual electric consumption for residential customers has increased 130 percent.

The increases in electricity consumption reflect the advantages of electricity over other energy forms. Electricity can be transported over long distances almost instantly. It is versatile enough to fulfill many different needs, from heating and cooling our homes to running the machinery upon which our industrial society is based. Moreover, it is a clean energy source at the point of use.

Unfortunately, the traditional methods for producing electricity eventually will prove either insufficient or unavailable. Environmental goals, concerns about depleting fuel resources, and national security considerations are combining to create new technological ground rules for electric power production. Alternative sources such as solar, wind, and geothermal energy may play an important role in insuring that U.S. citizens can continue to enjoy an adequate, reliable electricity supply in the years ahead.

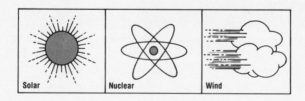

Solar   Nuclear   Wind

HOW ELECTRICITY IS PRODUCED TODAY

Essentially all electricity currently is produced in (1) plants that burn fossil fuels (which include coal, oil, and natural gas); (2) nuclear power facilities that are fueled by uranium; and (3) hydroelectric plants that rely on falling water. The largest portion of electricity is produced by burning coal, which accounted for nearly 51 percent of electricity production in 1980. Oil was used to produce nearly 11 percent of the nation's electricity in 1980, gas about 15 percent, uranium about 11 percent, and falling water about 12 percent.

How is electricity produced from fossil fuels?

In a fossil-fueled power plant, coal, oil, or natural gas is burned in a boiler to produce heat. The heat is used to change water into steam. The steam, under pressure, spins the blades of a turbine that, in turn, spins a generator. An electromagnet in the generator, turning inside a large coil of wire, produces electricity. After the steam passes through the turbine, it is condensed and recirculated to the boiler in a closed loop for reheating.

How is uranium used to generate electricity?

Uranium is used in nuclear power plants, which operate in a manner similar to fossil-fueled plants. The heat needed to produce the steam, however, comes from splitting atoms, a process called nuclear fission. The atoms are split in a device called a nuclear reactor that, in effect, replaces the power plant boiler.

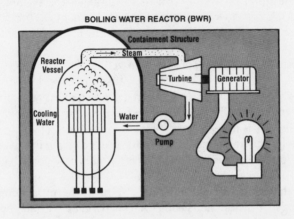

BOILING WATER REACTOR (BWR)

How does hydropower work?

A hydroelectric power plant uses the energy of falling water to produce electricity. The falling water turns a water turbine connected to a generator. This generation method is clean and relatively inexpensive, but its use is expected to grow only modestly in the years ahead because the number of potential sites is limited, although technological advances have made possible the use of some previously unsuitable sites.

One example is a fully-assembled hydroelectric power plant from France that recently was shipped to the small town of Vanceburg, KY. The 72-megawatt generating station traveled four weeks without ever touching dry land. The plant then was assembled on its preconstructed foundations at Greenup Dam. Designed to run submerged even in severe flood conditions on the Ohio, the plant employs innovative "bulb turbines" that can produce electricity in the low-head conditions—conditions under which dam heights are relatively low—that exist on many of the world's rivers.

What determines the type of energy source used to produce electricity?

The types of fuels an electric utility uses to generate electricity depend on a variety of factors, including price and availability. A utility's location plays a major role in determining which fuels are available in sufficient supply and which are the most reasonably priced. In the Pacific Northwest, for example, it would not be practical for utilities to rely heavily on oil because water sources to produce hydroelectric power are plentiful. Conversely, hydropower rarely is used in Texas or Oklahoma where gas historically has been the locally available fuel.

In an energy-intensive society such as ours, however, imported hydropower can make small but important contributions to the nation's fuel mix. Ontario Hydro, for example, recently was authorized to boost its electric power exports to the United States over the next ten years. The ruling allows 20 billion kilowatt-hours to be exported in any consecutive 12-month period from July 1, 1981 to December 31, 1983. Ontario Hydro's main markets are New York and Michigan, but a direct link with Pennsylvania also is planned: a 40-mile cable system across Lake Erie will be constructed jointly with General Public Utilities Corp.

THE NEED FOR IMPROVED AND NEW TECHNOLOGIES FOR PRODUCING ELECTRICITY

Research leading to the development of alternative electric energy sources is essential in the face of increasing oil and gas prices, environmental pressures, and growing electricity demand. Thanks to the efforts of scientists in both the private and public sector, technologies are within reach for expanding our use of domestic fossil fuel supplies and for tapping new energy sources.

Will the demand for energy exhaust the world's fossil fuel supplies?

Although fossil fuel supplies are plentiful, they also are non-renewable. As a result, they eventually will be exhausted if the world continues to use them to meet its energy needs. Some geologists estimate that 80 percent of the world's fossil fuel supply will be consumed over the next 300 years. That is a relatively short period of time when compared with the millions of years it took nature to create them.

Other authorities have suggested that, while the fossil fuel reserves that probably exist in the Western Hemisphere are enormous, social, political, economic, and technological factors will govern their availability. Because these supplies are finite, their depletion rates will be governed by electricity demand and by the speed with which renewable energy source technologies are developed to supplement them.

Who is doing the research to find new sources of electric energy?

Research always has been a key to the successful operation and continued improvement of electric utility systems. Individual researchers, as well as private companies, government agencies, research firms, and other organizations have worked separately and jointly to find new and better ways to produce electricity. In 1972, the electric utility industry, including investor-owned electric companies, electric cooperatives, and municipal utilities, sponsored the formation of the Electric Power Research Institute, (EPRI). EPRI will spend more than $1.5 billion for research in the next five years. In addition, many electric utilities are conducting their own experiments with alternative energy sources.

What is forecast for future energy needs?

Judgmental analysis and sophisticated economic and energy computer modeling can indicate ranges of potential energy use and availability. Edison Electric Institute recently commissioned a book-length study to analyze economic and energy prospects over the next 50 years. Called *Choice over Chance: Economic and Energy Options for the Future*, the book reveals a wide range of possibilities and outlines a preferred future based on two significant assumptions: continued economic growth to achieve society's goals, and the continuation of the historic link between energy use and employment. Since most people who will make up the labor force in the year 2000 have already been born, energy needs can be projected to at least that date with some degree of accuracy. Forecasts of energy consumption and electricity generation in the year 2000 are reprinted from the study's *Executive Summary* on page 95.

Why look at alternatives now?

Providing new energy sources for the future requires more than just good ideas. New technologies take time to mature. Just how much time and effort are involved in the transition from the laboratory to widespread commercial use depends on the type of technology involved, the size of devices to be manufactured, the complexity of the manufacturing system that must be established, and the type of market to be penetrated.

Recent experience shows that it takes 30 to 40 years for a new technology to evolve from idea to a significant generating source in the electric utility system. It took nuclear power, for example, more than 30 years to penetrate the electric utility industry market substantially, even though conditions were favorable.

For a new energy technology to be used widely, its cost must be low enough for it to compete economically with other technologies. The source must be effective, that is, able to provide enough energy to warrant the financial investment necessary to use it, and it must be reliable—proven to the point that both companies and customers will invest their money willingly and will be satisfied with the service they receive and the quantity of energy produced.

How do electric companies feel about new energy technologies?

Electric companies' primary objective is to provide their customers with an adequate and reliable electricity supply at the lowest possible cost. To accomplish this goal, electric companies are investing time, money, and manpower to find the best possible energy sources. Although they have no arbitrary allegiance to any particular energy source, utilities believe that, in the near term, the nation will have to rely on fossil-fueled and nuclear power plants to meet most of its electricity requirements. In the meantime, the industry is working to insure that

ENERGY CONSUMPTION IN THE YEAR 2000 (QUADS)

		SCENARIOS		
	1978	High	Preferred	Low
Consumption				
Oil....................................	34.7	45.2	25.6	13.6
Gas...................................	16.6	26.0	16.1	10.8
Coal..................................	4.0	8.2	9.4	7.6
Electricity	7.5	22.4	18.8	11.6
Syn. Oil, Gas & Shale	—	1.0	5.0	5.0
Solar Displacing				
Fossil Fuel	—	0.8	2.0	2.0
Electricity	—	1.2	3.0	3.0
Sub Total............................	62.8	104.8	79.9	53.6
Conversion Losses[1]	15.2	42.2	37.3	23.7
TOTAL	**78.0**	**147.0**	**117.2**	**77.3**

[1]*Does not include transportation and refining losses.*

ELECTRICITY GENERATION IN THE YEAR 2000

		SCENARIOS		
	1978	High	Preferred	Low
ENERGY INPUTS: (Quadrillion Btu)				
Coal....................................	10.1	39.7	29.1	11.1
Petroleum and Gas..............	6.6	3.1	3.6	3.0
Nuclear	2.9	18.0	18.0	15.8
Hydro and Other	3.1	3.4	3.4	3.4
TOTAL	**22.7**	**64.2**	**54.1**	**33.3**
% Coal	44.5	61.8	53.8	33.3
% Nuclear...........................	12.8	28.0	33.3	47.4
INSTALLED CAPACITY: (GW)				
Coal....................................	224	806	582	245
Oil and Gas Steam	161	170	170	170
Nuclear	52	300	300	270
Turbines.............................	50	183	146	50
Hydro and Other	74	86	86	86
TOTAL.................................	**561**	**1,545**	**1,284**	**821**
GENERATION:				
Trillion KWH......................	2.2	6.6	5.5	3.4
Percent of Delivered Energy..	11.9	21.4	23.5	21.6
KWH per Dollar of Real GNP	1.58	2.10	2.04	1.70
AVERAGE GROWTH RATES: (Percent/yr., 1978–2000)				
Energy Input.......................	—	4.8	4.0	1.7
Installed Capacity	—	4.7	3.8	1.7
Generation..........................	—	5.1	4.3	2.0

new energy technologies can make a significant contribution to meeting electricity needs as soon as possible.

FIRST STEP—USE ENERGY MORE EFFICIENTLY

While we strive to develop new and economical energy sources to maintain our quality of life, we must make better use of the energy now available. In every segment of our society, efforts are underway to use energy more efficiently.

Is conservation an energy resource?

When we use energy more efficiently, the effect is the same as if we have created additional energy. If, for example, we now can travel 36 miles in a car on one gallon of gasoline, when in the past we could travel only 12 miles on the same amount, in a sense we have created an extra two gallons of gasoline.

Almost all electric utilities have conservation programs, and some have as many as 30 or more designed to reach specified goals and industries. These range from programs promoting greater energy savings throughout the home to highly innovative projects involving aerial thermographic flyovers that produce photographs of heat loss from buildings and homes in an entire service area.

The United States has come to recognize the importance of conservation to its national energy security strategy. Despite conservation efforts, however, new power plants still will have to be built to meet future increases in electricity demand. To moderate the need for expensive new plants, many utilities are working to meet the demand for electricity as efficiently as possible.

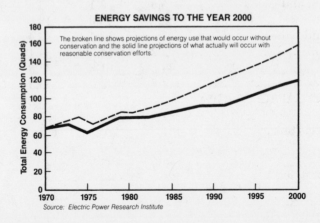

ENERGY SAVINGS TO THE YEAR 2000

The broken line shows projections of energy use that would occur without conservation and the solid line projections of what actually will occur with reasonable conservation efforts.

Source: Electric Power Research Institute

What is load management and what is its value?

Load management is the art of controlling the production and use of electricity to promote maximum efficiency in the use of an electric utility's generating capacity. Electricity must be generated at the moment it is needed. Thus, electric utilities must have enough generating capacity to meet the highest levels of customer demand, called peak levels, even though some of this capacity will not be used during periods of lower electricity demand. During periods of peak demand, utilities often rely on generating units that burn oil or natural gas to produce electricity. These so-called peaking units not only use more expensive fuels, but also are more expensive to operate. The goal of load management is to distribute customer electricity demand more evenly, thus moderating peak demand and allowing utilities' more economical generating units to provide a larger share of the electricity used by customers.

A primary load management technique is to encourage customers to shift some of their electricity use to off-peak hours, or hours when electricity demand is relatively low.

Is conservation enough?

Energy experts representing business, industry, universities, and government participated in an EPRI-sponsored conservation study to determine the maximum feasible energy savings our economy could achieve by the year 2000.

They concluded that although a 40 percent savings is technologically feasible, given economic realities, about 20 percent is more likely. Thus, although our use of energy will increase, it will increase less than it would without conservation.

SOME RENEWABLE ENERGY POSSIBILITIES

While research is underway to develop new advanced energy systems, there are materials at hand that can be converted to usable energy sources.

What is "biomass"?

Continuously renewable plants, trees, grass, algae, and industrial and municipal waste collectively are referred to as "biomass." Biomass undergoes a natural decomposition or decaying process, which produces useful gases such as methane. Research is being conducted on techniques for capturing this gas to produce energy.

Scientists from Pacific Gas and Electric Co. and Southern California Gas Co., for example, are converting cattle manure to methane gas at an experimental facility in the Imperial Valley. Using a process called anaerobic digestion, the facility produces about 7,000 cubic feet of methane daily from a ton of manure. The methane is used for boiler fuel at a nearby cattle feed mill. Use of manure is limited, however, since it is used to replenish minerals in farm land.

Another possibility being explored is the controlled harvesting of trees or other plants to produce boiler fuel. One obstacle, however, to using plants to fuel power plants is the large amount of land needed for their growth. Two hundred and eighty-five square miles of land would be needed, for example, to grow enough sycamore trees to continuously fuel a 200-megawatt power plant. About 50 square miles of land would be needed to grow enough sugar cane or sorghum for a 100-megawatt plant.

Other energy farms involving the joint efforts of electric utilities and firms using forest products may prove to be workable. A firm, for example, could use the portion of biomass material it needs, then provide a utility with the balance. Such an alternative and other similar ones currently are being studied.

Studies by EPRI and others have shown that, in certain regions of the country, small biomass-fired power plants using locally available mill residues may make technical and economic sense. A small Great Plains utility is planning to burn sunflower husks in a boiler originally designed for coal.

How practical is wood for producing energy?

Wood has been an energy source for thousands of years. As late as 1850, non-fossil energy sources met more than 90 percent of primary energy requirements in the United States. Now, with increases in prices for all energy sources, people again are looking at wood's potential. Trees, after all, are a renewable resource.

A federal government report entitled "Energy from Biomass Processes" says that wood as a fuel source has the potential for many applications. It can be burned directly in boilers or can be gasified to produce a fuel gas that can be burned in industrial boilers in place of oil or natural gas. Through more complex processing, wood can be converted into a liquid fuel similar to oil.

To date, several small power plants have been built using wood as a primary fuel. While site-specific applications have been successful, it remains to be seen whether a large-scale commercial venture would be practical. Our economy largely turned away from wood years ago because the supply had to be transported long distances.

Pacific Gas and Electric Co. and Louisiana Pacific Corp. are evaluating the commercial practicality of a wood-burning power plant. Wood waste from Louisiana Pacific's lumber mill in Samoa is used to produce steam for electricity generation. The steam also is used in the lumber company's wood product operations. Such multiple uses of steam are called "cogeneration."

Can we produce electricity from municipal waste?

Every person in the United States produces an estimated three to four pounds of garbage and trash a day. For the country as a whole, this amounts to 110 to 150 million tons of solid waste a year. Collecting and disposing of municipal solid waste is the third largest expenditure of local government, according to the National League of Cities.

There is potential for recovering energy and usable materials from this waste. Municipal solid waste consists of about 75 percent burnable materials, 8 percent metals, 10 percent glass, and 7 percent miscellaneous materials. Potential heat energy contained in unprocessed municipal solid waste is estimated at 9 to 9.4 million Btu per ton. This compares with 23 million Btu from a ton of coal and 6.2 from a barrel of oil.

To take advantage of this large potential energy source, problems related to the processing, handling, and burning of solid waste must be resolved. The present cost of producing energy from solid waste in general is greater than the value of the energy on the marketplace. Special modifications must be made to equipment to use fuel derived from waste. Futhermore, the waste must be collected and delivered to a power plant on a reliable basis, since it would make little sense for an expensive power plant to remain idle, at customer expense, waiting for garbage trucks to deliver fuel. Despite these problems, many electric utilities are studying various processes for utilizing municipal waste as a power plant fuel.

Plans are underway to build a $165 million resource-recovery plant on the Hudson River in Peekskill, NY that would convert between 365,000 and 657,000 tons of refuse a year into electricity. Since the 47-megawatt plant could provide twice the electricity that Peekskill needs, the Consolidated Edison Co. is expected to buy any excess electricity. The plant's construction is scheduled for 1984. The system, burning the refuse at 2,500 degrees Fahrenheit, would dispose of everything except ferrous metals, which would be sold for scrap, and certain other residue.

Solid waste, at best, could provide no more than four to seven percent of a utility's fuel requirements in a given area, and is unlikely to represent any significant cost savings. The serious societal problem of waste disposal, however, makes this fuel option increasingly significant.

ENERGY STORAGE—THE KEY TO MAKING ALTERNATIVE SOURCES USABLE

Production of electricity from alternative energy sources, such as solar or wind, has the disadvantage of not being readily controllable—that is, power may be produced when not needed and, alternatively, may not be available when needed. To make maximum use of these energy sources, some means must be developed to store the electric energy produced.

What alternative means of storing energy can be used now?

If a person were to think of one single thing to truly revolutionize the nation's energy systems, it would be to find an economic and reliable means of storing energy.

Alternative sources, such as solar and wind, are intermittent. In a solar system, for example, heat collected during the day, when the sun is shining, must be stored for use at night. Electricity itself cannot be stored directly in usable amounts. It must be tranformed into a different form of energy, such as chemicals in batteries, and reconverted when needed.

Electricity is produced and consumed at virtually the same moment. It goes from generator to point of use with nearly the speed of light. Consequently, electric companies must have sufficient production capacity available instantly to supply whatever amount the public demands.

If one were to use an alternative source such as the wind to produce electricity —without some kind of backup system—the wind would have to be blowing at all the times power was needed, and be blowing at sufficient strength and steadiness to provide the amount needed. Without some form of backup or storage, the wind is a highly unreliable source of power.

The need to provide a backup system seriously affects the cost of alternative systems. With solar energy systems, for example, heat could be stored in rocks or water until needed. However, such storage has limitations, and a hookup to some outside source is necessary. Thus, while the sunlight itself is free, collecting, storing, and using it reliably are not.

Lack of storage is a particularly acute problem for electric utilities and consumers that affects the cost of service. Companies must build expensive additional generating equipment to meet times of peak demand—for example, on a hot summer day when everyone wants air conditioning.

To help overcome this problem, utilities have developed "pumped storage"—a variation of conventional hydroelectric generation. Pumped storage uses and re-uses falling water to turn turbine-generators. Water is pumped uphill by electrically-driven pumps during periods when electricity is not needed by customers. Later, when customers' demands increase, the water is released to power a hydraulic turbine-generator. The cycle generally is repeated on a daily basis.

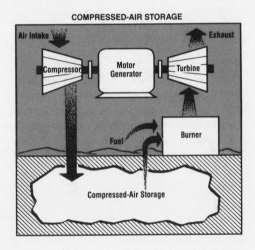

COMPRESSED-AIR STORAGE

What are the principal new methods under research for storing energy?

There is a need to find even more economical and reliable means of storing energy, and a number of methods are under research:

- *Compressed air.* A project in West Germany uses electric motors to compress air during times of little demand for electricity and stores the compressed air in underground caverns. When additional electricity is needed to meet consumer demand, the compressed air is released, spinning a turbine-generator.

  Expanding on the design of the West German compressed air energy storage plant (CAES), EPRI, the federal government, and turbomachinery manufacturers have made CAES a commercially available technology. EPRI has completed detailed engineering and cost studies of plants that utilize a variety of air storage reservoirs (salt domes, hard rock caverns, and aquifers) and require less "fuel" than the West German plant.

The first direct application of EPRI's work will be a commercial-scale CAES plant to be built by Soyland Power Cooperative in Decatur, Illinois. The 220-megawatt facility will use rock caverns to store compressed air until it is needed during peak generating periods. It is expected to save about 300,000 barrels of oil annually.

- *Underground* hydroelectric storage, an adaptation of the pumped-storage system previously described. Water, stored underground, is pumped up to reservoirs during periods of low electrical demand and allowed to run back down through turbine-generators to meet peak demand. Again, the problem is to find suitable locations.

- *Advanced battery systems.* Present battery technology uses lead plates and acid, as in automobile batteries. New ideas such as lithium/iron sulfide, zinc/chlorine, and sodium/sulfur are being examined in the hope of developing a battery with higher energy density (storage capacity), longer life, and lower production costs. EPRI has set a goal for battery cost of $300 a kilowatt of capacity. Several of the new technologies are coming close to that target figure now.

Real world testing of advanced battery systems is a goal of a project known as the Battery Energy Storage Test (BEST) facility located in Hillsborough Township in New Jersey. This 13-year, $14 million test facility, jointly sponsored by the federal government, EPRI, and Public Service Electric and Gas Co. of New Jersey, began operation in mid-1981.

- *Chemical conversion.* Chemical energy conversion systems other than batteries offer another possibility for energy storage. The production of burnable hydrogen from water is the most familiar example of a chemical energy conversion system. When electricity is applied to ordinary water, the water decomposes into hydrogen and oxygen—a process called electrolysis. Hydrogen could be produced by electrolysis during off-peak hours and stored in dispersed locations close to where it would be used to supplement gas or to generate electricity at periods of peak demand. Although hydrogen is an extremely versatile fuel, as an energy source it has two major drawbacks: large amounts of energy are needed to produce it, and its storage costs are presently much higher than for other systems. The same is generally true of other highly combustible chemicals that can be produced as storage mediums for the energy in surplus electricity.

- *Flywheels.* A *flywheel* is a device that can absorb, store, and release energy as required. Energy is stored when the wheel is rotated; i.e., when it has "momentum." When energy is withdrawn from the shaft as work, or is dissipated as friction, the wheel's rotation slows down. Flywheels commonly are used to smooth the pulsed power derived from engines. In the electric utility industry, energy stored in giant flywheels during off-peak hours would be used to drive generators at times of greater demand. Although flywheels have been used for centuries—as the basis of the potter's wheel, for example—they have not been practical for energy storage because of the large size and high speed they would require. Under such extreme conditions, the huge centrifugal forces generated could cause the wheel to fly apart. However, new designs and experimental materials hold some promise for solving this problem.

OTHER NEAR-TERM ENERGY TECHNOLOGIES

As the search for new answers goes on, man must look back to original energy sources—the sun and the wind—while proceeding to develop sophisticated technologies for producing synthetic fuels and other energy sources.

Can the sun's energy be used to make electricity?

The natural conversion of the sun's light energy occurs in the heating of the earth, the creation of winds and ocean waves, and the growth of plants. Solar technologies can convert this light energy into other energy forms. A major technology is solar power, the conversion of sunlight directly into electricity or, indirectly, into heat that is converted into electricity.

Generating electric power directly by the light of the sun involves "photovoltaic conversion," a process in which electricity is produced directly as a result of the absorption of sunlight (photons) by electrons within a semiconducting material such as silicon. The absorption frees the electrons (parts of atoms) and allows them to move—the movement actually constituting direct current electricity.

The photovoltaic phenomenon was discovered in 1839 but did not reach technical maturity until recently when space program applications were developed. Photovoltaic devices have been used with great success to provide energy for spacecraft and for some small terrestrial applications, such as remote beacons or floating buoys.

Large-scale commercial generating station applications are presently out of the question, however, due to the high cost. The idea of solar cells remains alluring, however, because the power is generated without boilers, turbines, generators, piping, or cooling towers. Once installed, these devices may need little maintenance. For a central power plant, the cell would be installed in large arrays with connecting wires. Photovoltaic conversion, however, requires more land area than thermal conversion. About two-and-a-half acres of cell area would be required to generate one megawatt of electricity at the source.

Currently, the major research effort is to reduce costs by improving manufacturing techniques. It will take a technological breakthrough before cheap, efficient photovoltaic devices are perfected. As in all the emerging technologies, the problem of storage also must be solved or the system will need a back-up to provide power when the sun is not shining.

Mass production of photovoltaic cells came a step closer during 1981 with delivery to Pacific Gas and Electric Co. of a five-square-foot solar cell module. One solar module is made up of 228 bits of silicon ribbon, each three-fourths of an inch wide and three-and-a-half inches long, and will produce about 60 watts of electric energy. The goal of the project is to bring the cost of solar cells, installed and ready to produce electricity, down from between the present $10 to $20 per installed watt, to $2 or less per watt by 1986.

A promising possibility for using the indirect method of converting sunlight into electricity is a solar-thermal electric generating station, which uses the heat of the sun to produce steam to drive conventional steam or gas turbines.

Current estimates indicate a central receiver system would cost less per kilowatt generated than other alternative solar-thermal generating plants. In one central receiver concept for a 100,000-kilowatt plant with six hours of storage, two identical reflector fields and towers would be employed. Each receiver would be perched atop an 80-story tower surrounded by a half-square-mile area covered with solar reflectors to track the sun during the day, reflecting beams to the receiver. This structure sometimes is referred to as the "power tower."

Temperatures could be generated at the receiver up to 1,500 degrees Fahrenheit, high enough to produce steam to run a turbine generating plant efficiently. However, significant materials problems encountered at these high temperatures must be resolved. A program testing a 5,000-kilowatt thermal facility has operated for several years. A 10,000-kilowatt central receiver demonstration plant that uses steam is expected to be operating by 1982. The Southern California Edison Co., the Los Angeles Department of Water and Power, the California Energy Commission, and the federal government are partners in the project.

Since these solar-thermal conversion power plants ideally would be sited in the arid regions of the southwestern United States where there is abundant sunshine, an EPRI program is evaluating the feasibility of alternative central tower concepts that do not have large cooling water requirements. One concept involves heating air instead of water to 1,500 degrees Fahrenheit in the receiver before running it through a turbine and a dry cooling tower.

There are other possibilities for solar-thermal plants that do not depend on a central tower. In such designs, each reflector concentrates solar energy on a separate receiver, and the fluid heated in the receivers is pumped through insulated pipes to a central power plant. There it is converted into steam for driving conventional turbine-generators.

Preliminary studies show the best potential for competitive solar-electric generation is the central receiver concept. Nevertheless, studies of other solar-thermal systems are underway to ensure that no potential source is overlooked in the drive to develop solar power generating systems as quickly as possible. In all cases, the expense of solar power plants, coupled with their inherently low reliability, will present a significant obstacle to widespread market penetration. They also may require large land areas—one of the problematical environmental impacts of solar energy. To supply the electric power needs for a city the size of Pittsburgh, for example, would require a collection area of about 30 square miles.

How does solar heating work?

Solar heating systems can be classified as either "passive" or "active." Passive systems contain essentially no moving parts and have minimal heat storage capability. Active systems are more sophisticated mechanically, involving equipment such as collectors, circulating pumps, and storage devices.

A passive system incorporates design features such as strategically placed windows, overhangs, and insulating materials. The orientation of the building is also important—it must be designed to capture the maximum heat from the sun during winter months.

For example, in addition to passive system design, an active system would employ special solar collectors in which a liquid such as water could be heated by the sun. This heated liquid would then be circulated to storage tanks where its heat energy could be used as needed.

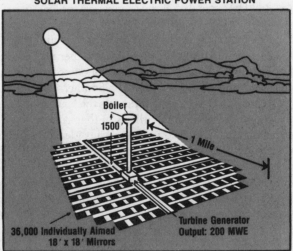

SOLAR THERMAL ELECTRIC POWER STATION

Boiler
1500'
1 Mile
36,000 Individually Aimed
18' x 18' Mirrors
Turbine Generator
Output: 200 MWE

How can solar heating be made more efficient?

One of the most promising technologies for expanding the use of solar energy is to employ it in tandem with a heat pump.

A heat pump works on the same principle as a room window air conditioner. An air conditioner pumps heat from inside a room to the outdoors—as one can see by holding a hand near the outside vent when the unit is running. A heat pump does the same thing, but much more efficiently. There is always some heat in the air regardless of the temperature. In the winter, a heat pump extracts heat from the outside and pumps it into the house. In the summer, the pump is reversed so it air-conditions the house by pumping heat to the outside.

The heat energy the heat pump takes out of the air is free—put there by the sun at no cost to the homeowner. Electricity to power the pump is the only cost of operation. The energy output of a heat pump will be greater than the energy input—up to three times greater under some conditions. This means for every dollar spent on heating energy, one can get up to three dollars worth of heat.

To further increase these benefits, electric utilities are investigating the possibility of combined heat pump-solar installations. When sufficient solar energy is available, it would be used to heat the home. During periods of low demand for electricity, the heat pump would replenish and boost the heat in the solar unit's storage system. This combination would provide a number of benefits:

- By supplementing solar energy, smaller areas would be needed for the solar collectors.
- If the heat storage was used up during a long cloudy spell, the heat pump would meet heating needs.
- The heat pump could operate at times when electricity demand is low, so electric companies could use abundant fuels—coal and nuclear—to generate the power, rather than expensive and increasingly scarce oil.

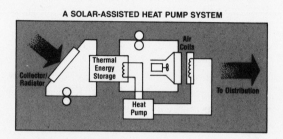

A SOLAR-ASSISTED HEAT PUMP SYSTEM

How can sunlight be stored?

If solar power is to be a reliable source of heat energy, both day and night, some form of storage is necessary. Low- and medium-temperature solar heat can be stored in water tanks or rock beds. Research is being done on fusible salt storage technology for future storage capabilities. However, all of these storage systems take up a great deal of space. For example, whereas water can store only about 120 Btu of solar-thermal energy per pound, coal provides between 10,000 to 12,000 Btu of heat energy per pound.

How would solar heating affect electric utilities?

Widespread use of solar energy would have various impacts on utilities. When solar heating is perfected, electric companies believe the prospect of it contributing substantially to the nation's energy mix will outweigh any difficulties they might encounter.

First, the nation's need for large quantities of electricity to power factories and create jobs will grow in the future, offsetting any decrease in electricity consumption resulting from the use of solar systems. Second, if properly integrated with utility systems, perhaps in tandem with electric heat pumps, solar heating could help utilities avoid wide fluctuations in peak demands. This would help avoid the construction of expensive generating equipment and help the nation reduce its dependence on oil. Third, the nation's housing stock changes slowly. A sudden shift to solar energy for substantial numbers of homes is as unlikely as it is expensive. Utilities will have time to adjust.

One problem, but again a surmountable one, involves backup heating and cooling systems for solar homes. Most often, these backup systems are electric.

Even though the backup might be used very little, utilities still have to provide sufficient generating capacity to meet the demand if all the backups come on at once—a possibility, for example, in a cold or cloudy spell lasting more than two or three days. Obviously, the expense of this additional generating capacity must be paid for by someone and, in fairness, it should be those benefiting from the service. For this reason, some utilities are considering "demand charges" to be paid by solar users whose systems contribute to such problems.

Can industry and agriculture use solar energy?

Solar energy has been used in agriculture for centuries to dry crops and grow products in greenhouses. Industrial applications have been much more modest, mainly limited to exposing something to the available sunlight. In some respects, the technology, as applied to heating residences and buildings, is generally applicable.

Some studies have been conducted on the application of existing solar heating technology on crop and grain drying and curing, food dehydration, and other farm applications. The results are inconclusive, and more analysis and experimentation are needed. The generation of low-to-medium quality steam appears to be the most promising industrial application, but there has not been enough experimentation and demonstration to reach reliable conclusions.

All of the technical problems, attributed to solar heating for residences, buildings, and schools are applicable to industrial and agricultural heating, with some major differences. Industry needs higher temperatures (350 degrees Fahrenheit) for its in-place systems. There will have to be considerable research, therefore, to find ways to elevate the temperature of the working fluids in solar systems.

Agriculture temperature demands are less stringent. However, the systems must be low in cost, reliable, and versatile enough to be used for many different jobs around the farm.

Would solar satellites solve some of the problems?

In space, there are no clouds to hide the sun, and the sun shines 24 hours a day, every day. Solar satellites have been proposed to take advantage of these factors. Energy collected by the satellites would be converted to microwaves and transmitted to earth.

Many of the technical problems associated with a satellite power station are well worth studying since most are fundamental to future manned and unmanned space flights. There is presently insufficient evidence, however, that this application of technology will contribute to the national energy budget any time soon.

In view of their cost and other related problems, orbiting solar power plants are not expected to become a reality until well into the twenty-first century.

What is being done to advance solar power?

A worldwide effort to develop methods of tapping the sun's energy is underway. In the United States, the federal government is involved extensively in solar research. EPRI has programmed $30 million over the next five years on solar research and development. A number of utilities with independent solar programs will invest more millions in projects related to the specific needs and potential of the regions they serve. A recent survey showed 236 electric utilities are sponsoring 840 solar research projects.

EPRI is funding ten solar-assisted space-conditioning houses. Five were built as a cooperative venture between building contractors and Long Island Lighting Co. in the Northeast, and five with Public Service Co. of New Mexico in the Southwest. The houses are highly instrumented to gather information on solar-assisted heating and cooling under actual conditions. Similar programs are underway for commercial and light industrial buildings.

Consolidated Edison Co. is beginning a two-year project to provide solar-assisted water heating systems to 700 houses in New York City and Westchester County. The solar systems are expected to provide about half the annual hot water needs of the homes in which they are installed. During the summer, the systems are expected to meet almost all the hot water needs.

Wisconsin Electric Power Co. has sold 160 solar water heating panels to its customers. The company says a family of four in Wisconsin can expect the sun to supply about half of its annual hot water needs. A survey of customers already involved in the project found many of them were able to shut off their electric backup system for the water heaters in the summer of 1980 because the solar units provided all of their hot water. Even on cloudy or cold days, the systems have provided a good portion of hot water needs.

Is the wind a practical source of energy?

Recent advances in wind-turbine technology, plus the increasing cost of fossil fuels, have improved the prospects for widespread use of wind power. These developments have led to increased activity in wind-power research within the electric utility industry. A 1980 EPRI survey identified some 91 utilities involved with 152 wind-power research projects, nearly double the activity identified in the previous year.

Satisfactory operating performance over extended time periods and cost-effectiveness for modern wind-turbine concepts have not yet been demonstrated, and, like solar technologies, wind turbines are an intermittent source of energy. However, they may make an important contribution to America's energy mix as early as the 1990s if existing research and development programs accomplish their overall objectives.

Wind-power development will be restricted to places where there are good wind resources. Hawaii, the Central Plains, and parts of the Pacific Northwest and California are particularly attractive for wind development. But even in parts of the country that do not enjoy broadly prevailing high winds, a few good sites for wind turbines may exist because wind characteristics are highly site-specific.

Several experimental large wind turbines have been designed, built, and tested during the past few years through a number of government and privately-sponsored programs. Experiences from these programs are being used to develop more advanced turbines with improved cost and performance characteristics. The coming years will see ongoing evaluation of both existing wind turbines and additional machines based upon new designs.

Generally, it is believed that wind power's greatest potential is in displacement of fossil fuel use during windy periods, rather than displacement of planned generating capacity. In fact, because of the intermittent nature of the wind resource, initially little or no capacity displacement is likely as a result of wind power. If the cost of wind turbines declines enough in the future, however, their fuel-displacement value alone may justify them.

CONVENTIONAL WIND TURBINE

How are utilities utilizing wind power?

Electric utilities are playing a major role in advancing wind power development, not only by conducting their own projects, but by utilizing wind-generated electricity others have produced.

A 600-kilowatt windfarm constructed by New England Electric Systems and operated by U.S. Windpower, for example, is generating power on a windy ridge of Crotched Mountain in Greenfield, NH. The facility is expected to produce 1.5 million kilowatt-hours each year, or enough energy for 150 to 200 typical New England homes. Electricity generated by the twenty 30-kilowatt windmills is purchased by Public Service Co. of New Hampshire.

Reversing the usual role of electric utilities, Southern California Edison Co. recently has offered to buy wind-generated power from its customers. It invited proposals "for the sale of electricity generated by wind parks."

Pacific Gas and Electric Co., together with Windfarms, Ltd. and the California Department of Water Resources, is negotiating a contract under which the utility and the state agency would buy electricity produced at a windfarm to be built in Solano County, CA. The generating facility, scheduled for completion in 1989, would include 146 wind-powered turbine generators with a capacity of 350,000 kilowatts. The utility said the project could produce nearly one billion kilowatt-hours of electricity a year.

DRY STEAM GEOTHERMAL POWER CYCLE

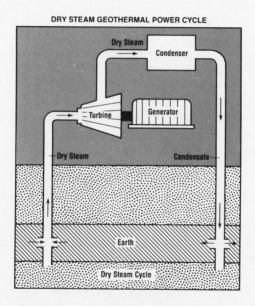

What is geothermal energy?

"Geothermal" energy comes from within the earth. It is created by the decay of radioactive substances, by chemical reactions, by friction from the movement of the continents, and by heat present when the earth was formed. The most famous example of geothermal energy can be observed approximately every 60 minutes at Yellowstone National Park when the geyser "Old Faithful" erupts in a fascinating display of one of nature's more predictable emotions.

There are four basic forms of geothermal energy: dry steam, hot water or wet steam, geopressurized systems, and hot dry rock. Dry steam is produced when hot water boils in an underground reservoir and some of the resulting steam flows to the surface under pressure. It is the cheapest and simplest form of geothermal energy. Unfortunately, dry steam occurs only in a few places, and the United States' resources are quite limited.

Dry steam is found, for example, at The Geysers, about 90 miles north of San Francisco. At this site, Pacific Gas and Electric Co. operates the world's largest generating plant using the earth's heat to produce electricity. More than 900 megawatts of electricity are produced from this plant, enough to meet the electricity needs of half of San Francisco. By the 1990s, Pacific Gas and Electric Co. hopes to expand this facility to generate 2,000 megawatts—approximately the capacity of two Hoover Dams or two large fossil-fueled or nuclear-powered units.

Hot water or wet steam is the next most attractive form of geothermal energy. It is created when underground water is heated by surrounding hot rock or magma (molten rock at temperatures as high as 2,200 degrees Fahrenheit), and remains liquid because of underground pressure. This super-hot water, mixed with some steam, flows to the surface when wells are drilled in the correct places.

Southern California's Imperial Valley has the most accessible sources of hot water geothermal energy known in the United States. San Diego Gas and Electric Co., in partnership with other utilities, the federal government, and EPRI, is designing a 45-megawatt power plant to operate on a 360-degree Fahrenheit hot-water reservoir at Heber in the Imperial Valley. This plant will use a new process, known as binary-cycle conversion, to generate electricity. In this process, the geothermal fluid transfers its heat to a second fluid, called the working fluid, that has a boiling point low enough to vaporize when it is heated by the hot water. This vapor then drives a turbine to generate electricity. With the better thermodynamic properties of the working fluids in binary-cycle systems—fluids such as isobutane—lower-temperature hot water can be used. As a result, the binary-cycle technology is expected to become the preferred power generating method for about half of the identified hot-water geothermal resources in the United States.

Southern California Edison Co. (SCE) has contracted with two geothermal resource companies for development of three power plant projects in the Imperial Valley. One of these projects has produced a detailed design for a flashed steam power plant using the moderate-temperature, low-salinity hot water from the Heber reservoir. The other two projects involve the construction of 10-megawatt power plants operating with high-temperature, high-salinity resources at Brawley and the Salton Sea in the Imperial Valley. The Brawley plant has been in operation since the summer of 1980. The Salton Sea site has been used for tests of methods to handle the high-salinity brine, and the plant itself is being designed.

Geopressurized systems are reservoirs of hot water mixed with methane gas trapped underground at high pressures in sediments of impermeable shale. Reservoirs have been found on the Gulf Coast during petroleum exploration but have not been developed because supplies are uncertain and drilling is expensive. The most common form of geothermal energy is hot dry rock and magma. A substantial amount of this resource has been found in the West, but development is in the experimental stage. Energy production from this source will require more advanced technology to be economically feasible.

As with any naturally occurring phenomena, there are always uncertainties and unknowns. No two geothermal fields in the world are exactly alike. Each presents different hopes, unexpected disappointments, and new problems.

There are environmental problems, too. In using dry steam, for example, the steam must be vented to clear the lines and to test or protect wells. This venting releases quantities of hydrogen sulfide, ammonia, and radon, and can be noisy unless adequately muffled. Dissolved minerals in the steam create corrosion problems for pipes, valves, and the turbine.

Research sponsored by EPRI is finding ways to combat these undesirable components of geothermal fluids. An experimental system recently tested at The Geysers successfully removed an average 95 percent of hydrogen sulfide and other noncondensable gases while reducing efficiency of the plant very little. Other research is directed toward more fully understanding scaling and corrosion properties of geothermal fluids. Research is being done on utilizing the energy in geopressured and hot-rock systems as well, although more advanced technologies will be required to obtain power from these sources. Electric utilities, the federal government, EPRI, and other segments of the nation's industry are exploring the development of geothermal energy.

What is a fuel cell?

Using fuel without "burning" it, a fuel cell works like a storage battery, producing electricity from a chemical reaction with little waste heat or gas. Fuel cells were discovered in 1839, but it has taken many years of research and development to bring them to even limited use.

Fuel cells have a number of advantages over other methods of producing electricity. They utilize fuel very efficiently and do not pollute the air. Because they are environmentally acceptable, fuel cells could be placed in cities where energy use is very high—saving transmission line costs.

EPRI and the federal government are researching ways to improve fuel cell efficiency and to lower capital costs. They now are funding a 4.8-megawatt commercial prototype fuel cell that is being evaluated by Consolidated Edison of New York. If all goes well with this program, commercialization of fuel cells may be a reality by 1985.

Fuel cell power plants appear to be economically attractive options for peaking and intermediate power demands. Since these plants can be located close to where the electricity would be used, transmission line costs could be reduced. Waste heat from the fuel cell could be used for space and water heating in housing complexes and shopping centers.

Potentially, fuel cells can achieve significant savings in fuel, energy costs, and capital investment. They are environmentally clean. Additional research, however, must verify that the systems have adequate endurance and that their costs are competitive enough to assure successful commercialization.

What new technologies are being developed to make better use of coal?

Coal is an ample energy resource in the United States and can be used to supplement or replace scarce oil and gas. New technologies are needed to improve the ways we use coal, however, either by burning it more cleanly or by converting it to liquid or gaseous fuels at a competitive cost.

- Fluidized-bed combustion (FBC) is a method of reducing emissions by controlling and modifying the various chemical reactions that are present during the burning of regular coal. Gases that might pollute the air or have other undesirable effects are prevented from forming or are converted to other compounds that are harmless.

The crushed coal burns in what is known as a fluidized bed: a concentrated suspension of crushed limestone particles in a flow of hot gas, usually air. The bed is composed mostly of solids, but the movement of hot air causes the particles to roll. The turbulence of the churning bed allows excellent mixing of the coal, air, and limestone and keeps the temperature stable. As the coal burns, the limestone removes sulfur gas by-products by reacting with them to form calcium sulfate, a disposable solid waste.

- Coal conversion processes clean up coal before it is burned. In the liquefaction process, crushed coal plus a chemical solvent form a slurry that dissolves under high heat and pressure in the presence of hydrogen. Unwanted by-products are removed by separation processes and low-sulfur liquid fuel is recovered. This type of liquid fuel could be used in existing oil-fired power plants without major plant modification.

- The gasification process produces a clean, burnable gas from coal. When coal is burned conventionally, nearly all of the chemical energy is released as heat energy. If the amount of oxygen is restricted and the temperature and duration of the reaction are controlled, the chemical energy in the coal will be released in the form of gases that will burn, such as hydrogen and carbon monoxide. The device that can accomplish this is called a gasifier.

Coal gasification has been in use throughout the world for many years. Gasified coal, like coal liquids, however, cannot compete economically with natural liquid and gaseous fuels given today's technologies. EPRI, the federal government, and other industries have research programs underway to facilitate the commercialization of liquefaction and gasification processes.

FUTURE TECHNOLOGIES

The search must continue for commercially attractive, clean sources of energy for generating the electricity our nation needs. There are several long-range programs underway to research new technologies with still unpredictable futures.

Are the nuclear energy technologies of the fast breeder reactor and fusion promising alternatives?

- Breeder reactors are designed to produce more fissionable material than they consume and to generate electric power simultaneously. In this way, they have the potential for extending the world's uranium reserves for centuries while providing much-needed electrical power. In fact, the uranium already mined and in storage, using breeder reactors, could generate as much electricity as 580 billion tons of coal—one and one-third times the nation's demonstrated coal reserve.

The breeder reactor can produce 50 times more energy from a pound of uranium than can be produced now in a current nuclear reactor. In fact, the neutrons produced in present nuclear power reactor systems are being wasted and could be used productively to breed new fuel. Once the present abundant source of neutrons, that is, the fissionable U-235, has been depleted (the U-235 resource is limited), no similar neutron source is available. Every day of present design power reactor operation loses forever the neutrons that could create valuable fuel.

Development of breeder reactors in other countries continues at an increasing pace. Large-scale demonstration breeder reactors presently are producing electricity in the Soviet Union (2 reactors), France (1), Great Britain (2), and Japan (1).

- Scientists have been working for over 25 years to control fusion as a power source. It may well be the most difficult technical task ever attempted, but the potential of fusion energy is enormous. There is enough deuterium—the fuel for fusion—in the world's oceans to supply the current energy needs for billions of years, and the cost of extracting that deuterium is likely to be small.

For fusion reactions to take place, the high temperature gases must be held at certain minimum temperatures and densities. These conditions have been described as plasma confinement for at least one second at 100 million degrees Celsius at a density of about 100–1000 trillion (10^{12}) nuclei per cubic centimeter. Under these conditions, fusion can take place, releasing new helium nuclei, some free neutrons, and heat, which could be extracted for power generation.

Fusion power plants are inherently safe against "runaway reactions" since they contain only as much fuel as they can burn. Although the internal structure would become radioactive through neutron bombardment, the waste products of the fusion reaction itself are nonradioactive.

Work on fusion is continuing since the possible payoff of virtually unlimited energy supply is enormous. Fundamental research is still necessary, however, and in the absence of additional evidence the fusion reactor should not be considered a contributor to the national energy budget much before the middle of the next century. Electric utilities have allocated funds already to assure the availability of fusion reactors for maximum usefulness as quickly as possible.

What is magnetohydrodynamics?

The phenomenon of magnetohydrodynamics (MHD) produces electricity directly from heated gases, rather than by the mechanical spinning of a generator. The idea is to pass high-temperature ionized gases through a powerful magnetic field. This produces a flow of electrons in the gases. This flow of electrons, when collected and transferred to an outside circuit, constitutes an electric current.

High efficiencies are in prospect for this process. It can be used in combination with existing turbogenerators, since the heat remaining in the superheated gases is still enough to make steam to power the existing turbines.

Magnetohydrodynamics (MHD) has been studied since the early 1940s. Two types of MHD generators are being considered. In one, the open cycle, the combustion gases form the conducting plasma, which is seeded with potassium carbonate or similar substances to promote ionization. Ionizing temperatures of from 3,400 to 4,700 degrees Fahrenheit are required, so the inlet air to the combustor must be preheated. The heat remaining in the expended combustion gas is used to provide heat for a conventional steam generating plant.

The second type of MHD generator maintains the plasma material separately from the combustion gases and uses heat exchangers to transfer the heat to the plasma. Typically, the plasma would be an inert gas such as argon seeded with cesium vapor. The ionization temperatures for the closed cycle MHD are around 3,000 degrees Fahrenheit.

After more than 30 years of investigation, however, there still are no clear-cut figures on the contribution MHD would make to the national energy budget. In combination with existing technology, MHD is expected to raise the efficiency of a steam plant by more than 15 percent. An investment of several billion dollars will have to be made to bring the technology up to a commercial stage.

While the technology is feasible, many problems remain. There are serious questions, for example, about recovery of the expensive seeding material, durability of some equipment, reliability of the electrodes, and performance of the superconducting magnet. Plant capital costs, durability, and emission controls are also major questions to be resolved.

MHD AND STEAM TURBINE-GENERATORS IN COMBINED CYCLE

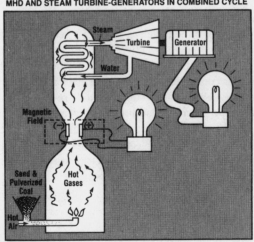

Is the thermal energy in the ocean useful?

The idea of extracting useful work from the thermal energy in the world's oceans has been an attraction for over 100 years. Ocean thermal energy conversion (OTEC) is entering the engineering feasibility phase of the development process. Unlike other forms of solar energy, OTEC is most attractive for baseload—that is, full-time—generation of electricity.

The OTEC concept involves utilizing the temperature difference between warm surface waters and cold deep water to vaporize a fluid such as ammonia or propane. This vapor would then be used to drive a turbine generator to produce electricity.

Because of the small temperature difference involved, 35 degrees Fahrenheit or less, an OTEC plant would be very inefficient and would therefore require enormous equipment for relatively small amounts of power. One proposed design for an ocean thermal plant has an upper module 790 feet in diameter and 100 feet deep, with a cold water intake pipe 1,500 feet deep and 100 feet in diameter. The warm and cold ocean water would be pumped at about 6 billion gallons per hour (about one-third the flow of the Mississippi). The plant would have to be located 20 to 150 miles offshore to obtain the necessary water depth. This would necessitate a long and costly underwater transmission line.

In addition to the great expense associated with such a large plant, the engineering task of designing a structure to operate in a corrosive marine environment is formidable. The environmental impacts of an ocean thermal power plant are not known, but several can be identified. Mixing deep ocean water with surface water, for example, would vary the oxygen concentration of the ocean. The impact upon marine life is not known.

The French have been the most active in this technology, having installed several small systems. The direction most advocates recommend is to use OTEC installations to offset energy use in the continental U.S. For example, aluminum could be produced at sea and save electrical energy presently consumed in the United States. There is also the option of industrializing islands in the tropics and sub-tropics using off-shore power plants as a source of electricity.

The OTEC concept still requires a thorough investigation of the hardware requirements and the economics of installation and operation. In view of the obstacles and cost estimates to date, ocean thermal power is not expected to make a significant contribution to national electricity generation.

Can ocean motion—the tides—generate power?

Those who have had the experience of swimming in the ocean know waves pack a wallop and tides exert a strong pull. These forms of energy, too, are under study for possible use. So are the "rivers" in the oceans, such as the Gulf Stream and the Arctic Current.

A tidal power system operates in much the same way as a hydroelectric dam. A dam is constructed across a coastal inlet. The incoming tide runs through turbines in the dam, turning a generator to produce electricity. As the tide drops, the water runs out of the reservoir through the turbines, again generating electricity.

There are several advantages to tidal power. The energy of moving ocean water is free. Because tides depend on the unchanging cycles of the moon, tidal power would be intermittent but possibly more reliable than some other hydropower forms that can be affected by drought.

Unfortunately, there are only a limited number of places in the world where the tidal range—the difference in elevation between low and high tide—is great enough to justify construction. In the United States, the only possible sites are Passamaquoddy Bay in northern Maine, Puget Sound in the Northwest, and the south coast of Alaska. Even these sites have problems—they have more desirable uses and are too far from places where the power is needed.

There are only two operating tidal plants. One is a 400-kilowatt unit at Kislaya Guba in the Soviet Union; the other is a 240,000-kilowatt unit at La Rance, France. There are no statistics on the Soviet plant, but the cost of electricity from the French plant is not competitive with costs from other methods of generating electricity.

OCEAN-THERMAL ENERGY CONVERSION PLANT

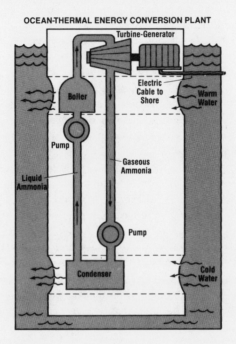

Can energy be extracted from waves?

Concepts for extracting energy from waves fall into three categories: using the vertical rise and fall of waves to power either water or air turbines; using to-and-fro motion to turn turbines or to apply pressure intermittently against various oscillating devices; and converging waves into a trough or channel to maintain a "head" of water to drive turbines (i.e. to use the weight of falling water).

The Japanese utilize the up-and-down motion of waves to compress air to drive a small generator in a lighthouse. England has a modest research program for developing the contoured rocking vane or "Salter cam" and other wave energy conversion technology. Very little work is being done in the United States.

Studies indicate that producing the equivalent of the 2,000-megawatt power generated by the Columbia River dams would require collecting all the wave power from about 62 miles of the Oregon Coast at the rate of 32 megawatts a mile of coastline.

Using the swift currents in ocean waters, expecially those off Florida, to produce work has been proposed for many years. The intent is to translate the current movement to rotating motion by water wheel, Kaplan turbines, propeller turbines, and vertical axis turbines.

To date, very little has been done to bring this concept closer to reality. Very large equipment would be required, and it would have to be placed close to the water surface. There will have to be substantial mooring to withstand higher currents and storms. No studies have been conducted on salt water effects on machinery, fouling of the equipment by marine life, equipment reliability, or interference with navigation.

SOURCES

Numerous scientific and informational sources were used to produce this chapter. In addition to Edison Electric Institute, the sources include several federal agencies, Electric Power Research Institute, National Petroleum Council, Chemical Engineering Magazine, the Energy Research Group, EUA Service Corp., Central Power and Light Co., and Central and South West Corp.

WHERE TO CALL FOR ADDITIONAL INFORMATION

Individually, electric companies have many research and development programs underway. If you want additional information, the electric company providing service in your area is likely to have it. Call the company first—people there might be working on that very idea.

Other sources include:

Edison Electric Institute
Washington, DC
202/828-7400

Electric Power Research Institute
Palo Alto, CA
415/855-2000

Atomic Industrial Forum, Inc.
Washington, DC
301/654-9260

American Nuclear Society
La Grange Park, IL
312/352-6611
Arlington, VA
703/521-8806

Scientists and Engineers for
Secure Energy, Inc.
Washington, DC
202/223-5381

INDEX

Abnormalities, developmental, 30
Accident analysis, 16
The accident at Three Mile Island, 7, 20-21, 29-33
  Presidential Commission on, 20-21, 30
Accidents, 19-21, 33, 37-38
  in coal mines, 70
  conditions of, 16
  expenses of, 31
  laboratory, 41
  loss-of-cooland, 49
  nuclear, 24, 31 (*see also* The accident at Three Mile Island)
Acidification of lakes, 79
Acid mine drainage, 68-69
Acid rain, 13, 67, 76-81
ACRS (*see* Advisory Committee on Reactor Safeguards)
Active solar heating systems, 103-105
Adirondack Mountains, 79
Advisory Committee on Reactor Safeguards (ACRS), 12, 49
AEC (*see* Atomic Energy Commission)
Aerial thermographs, 96
Agencies, state, 19
Agriculture, solar energy used in, 106
Air
  compressed, 100-101
  containment, 32
  contaminated, 32
  radiation from, 27
  samples of, 17
Air conditioning, 1, 6, 100, 104
Air pollution, 7, 19, 22, 67
  from coal combustion, 76-79, 111-112
  in coal mines, 70
Air pollution controls, cost of, 78
Air storage reservoirs for compressed air, 100-101
Air turbines, 116
Alabama, 51, 67
Alabama Power Co., 51
Alaska, 35, 116
Allens Creek 1 (nuclear power plant), 59
Allis-Chalmers, 51, 60
Alpha particles, 22
Alternative energy systems, 5, 7, 91-118
  backup systems for, 99-100, 105-107
  costs of, 99-103
  technologies for, 7, 47, 91-118
Aluminum, 1, 115
Alvin W. Vogtle 1 and 2 (nuclear power plants), 53
American Nuclear Society (ANS), 49, 61, 118
American Revolution, 5
American Society of Mechanical Engineers (ASME), 49
Ammonia, 111, 115-116

Animals, health damage studies on, 77
ANS (*see* American Nuclear Society)
Anthracite, definition of, 66
Appalachia Regional Commission, 69
Appliances, electric, 75, 86
Applications for building nuclear reactors, 12
Aquatic life, 14
Arab oil embargo, 4
Arid regions of the United States, solar-thermal conversion plants in, 103
Argon, 114
Argonne National Laboratories, 2
Arizona, 51, 67, 73
Arizona Public Service Co., Salt River Project, 51
Arkansas, 52, 73
Arkansas Nuclear One-1 and One-2, 52
Arkansas Power & Light Co., 52
Arlington (Oregon), 57
Arlington (Virginia), 61, 118
Arsenic, 41
Arctic Current, 115
Ash, 76-78, 81-82
ASLB (*see* Atomic Safety and Licensing Board)
ASME (*see* American Society of Mechanical Engineers)
Atmosphere, 48
Atomic bombs, 19-20, 24, 42-43
Atomic Energy Commission (AEC), 49
  (*see also* Department of Energy; Nuclear Regulatory Commission)
Atomic Energy Commissioner, 25
Atomic Industrial Forum, 27n, 61, 118
Atomic Safety and Licensing Board (ASLB), 12
Atomic weapons, 19-20, 24, 41-43
Atomic weights, 9
Atoms, 9
  unstable, 22
Australia, 19
Automobiles, electric, 1, 3
Auxiliary systems, 16
Avila Beach (California), 52

Babcock & Wilcox (B&W), 51-52, 54-55, 57-58, 60
Background radiation, 22-24, 27-28
Backup systems for alternative energy, 99-100, 102, 105-107
Bacteria, 14
Baghouses, definition of, 77
Balanced systems, 9
Bailly Nuclear 1 (nuclear power plant), 54
Baltimore Gas and Electric Co., 54
Barges, transportation of coal by, 71-72, 85
Barriers, 16-17

119

134

DATE DUE

GAYLORD			PRINTED IN U.S.A.